英文學了不使用，就會忘記。
每天唸「英文一字金」，就是在使用英文。

英文單字有17萬多個，
一字多義，無人背得完。
學會「常用7000字」，
可看懂90%的英文。

背每天都可用到的短句，
是學英文最佳的方法。
「英文一字金」是短句中的短句。

每天背「英文一字金」，
沒有煩惱，天天在進步，有成就感。

# 爲什麼一背會上癮？

　　我們聽別人的勸告，大部份的人都不會改變，因爲大道理你天天聽，天天忘記。但是，如果我們天天背：*Advance*.（要進步。）*Attain*.（要達到目標。）*Acquire*.（要有收穫。）不停地背，背到變成直覺，自然而然就會改變了。大家都要進步，有誰做到？你天天唸「英文一字金」，唸了一千遍 *Advance*.（要進步。），你被洗腦，就自然會付諸行動，向前進。

　　人類追求長壽，要活得久，最大的祕訣，就是要快樂。這本「快樂幸福經」（How to Be Happy），背完你就快樂了。小孩成長、大人進步（advance），是最快樂的事。你的目標達成了（attain）、有收穫（acquire），更是令人快樂。每天只要背 *Advance. Attain. Acquire.* 三個字，三句話，沒有煩惱，非常愉快。

　　有的人要死不活，一臉痛苦的表情，苦瓜臉，人人避之惟恐不及。我們每天都要充滿活力，*Be alive*.（要充滿活力。）*Be animated*.（要有活力。）有人不看電影、不畫畫、不跳舞、不唱歌，當然不會快樂，所以要 *Be artistic*.（要懂得欣賞藝術。）

　　我認識一位劉醫師，存了很多錢，還是租房子住。我帶他去買了一戶房子，他立刻高興得不得了。我跟他說，你得到的快樂，超過你所有的花費。我們一定要 *Seek adventure*.（要尋求冒險。）只要沒有生命危險的，都要嘗試。吃沒吃過的東西，去沒去過的地方，認識新朋友，都是一種冒險。有人怕見陌生人、怕交新朋友，自我封閉，沒有學到新東西，沒有新資訊、沒有改變，當然不快樂。

「快樂幸福經」第一回 A 開頭的九句話，會讓你非常快樂。背背看，很容易。*Advance.–Attain.–Acquire.* 這三個動詞先背，是不是一分鐘就可以背下來？再背 *Be alive.–Animated.–Artistic.* 三個形容詞；Seek *adventure.–Amusement.–*Go *abroad.* 兩個名詞，一個副詞。只要背完這九句話，你一定會迷上「快樂幸福經」。

　　你可能不知道，洗個澡（Shower.）、去買個東西（Shop.）、去唱歌（Sing.），這些看來很小的事情，一點一滴都會讓你快樂。你天天背：*Shower. Shop. Sing.* 你就會不知不覺受到影響。有些人什麼都複雜化，忙得昏頭轉向，**如果背：*Simplify. Live simply. Seek serenity.* 你就知道什麼都要簡化、要過簡單的生活，要尋求寧靜。**唯有背多，背到變成直覺，才能讓你改變，否則你還是你，改變太難了。

　　自從我開始背「英文一字金」以來，自己感覺到進步很大，朋友越來越多，事業越來越順利，心情越來越愉快。難怪有人肯拋棄一切、親人，出家、做修女，原來，他們最大的快樂是「唸經」。

　　我每天早晨到公園裡，一面運動，一面背「英文一字金」。無聊的時候，嘴裡唸唸有辭。晚上睡覺，躺在床上，心中也會默背。**最大的收穫，不只是英文單字增加，更重要的是思想、行為的改變。**如我常背：*Rest. Risk. Be relaxed.* 無形中，我一感到累的時候，就會休息（Rest.），不會硬撐。很多人一點險都不敢冒（Risk.），存了很多的錢，天天看著鈔票，結果錢逐年貶值，自己吃大虧。無論發生什麼事，都要放輕鬆（Be relaxed.），緊張對身體有害。我每天背「英文一字金」，每天修正，每天改變，每天進步，身體越來越好。

劉毅

**How to Be Happy**

# *1.* A

| 看英文唸出中文 | 一口氣說九句 | 看中文唸出英文 |
|---|---|---|

**advance**[2]
〔əd'væns〕 v.

**attain**[6]
〔ə'ten〕 v.

**acquire**[4]
〔ə'kwaɪr〕 v.

三個動詞

> *Advance.*
> 要進步。
>
> *Attain.*
> 要達到目標。
>
> *Acquire.*
> 要有收穫。

前進

達到

獲得

---

**alive**[2]
〔ə'laɪv〕 adj.

**animated**[6]
〔'ænə,metɪd〕 adj.

**artistic**[4]
〔ɑr'tɪstɪk〕 adj.

三個形容詞

> Be *alive.*
> 要充滿活力。
>
> *Animated.*
> 要有活力。
>
> *Artistic.*
> 要懂得欣賞藝術。

活的

有活力的

藝術的

---

**adventure**[3]
〔əd'vɛntʃə〕 n.

**amusement**[4]
〔ə'mjuzmənt〕 n.

**abroad**[2]
〔ə'brɔd〕 adv.

二個名詞

> Seek *adventure.*
> 要尋求冒險。
>
> *Amusement.*
> 要尋求娛樂。
>
> Go *abroad.*
> 要出國。

冒險

娛樂

到國外

**A**

## I. 背景說明：

我們把 Advance. Attain. Acquire. 當作口號來背，通常在句中，attain 和 acquire 是及物動詞。*Advance*. 的意思有：①要進步。（= *Improve*.）②要向前進。（= *Move forward*.）可説成：Always be *advancing*.（永遠要進步。）Find a way to *advance* your knowledge.（要找到能增加知識的方法。）advance 可作「前進；進步；增加」解。*Attain*. 可説成：*Attain* your goals.（要達到你的目標。）Get pleasure from *attaining* a goal.（要從達到目標中獲得快樂。）*Acquire*. 可説成：*Acquire* valuable knowledge.（要獲得有價值的知識。）*Acquire* fluency in a foreign language.（外語要能説得流利。）（= *Be fluent in another language*.）acquire 的意思有：①獲得②學到。

*Be alive*.（= *Be full of animation and activity*.）*Be alive* and ready for action.（要有活力，隨時準備行動。）*Be alive* and alert.（要有活力又有警覺。）alive 的意思有：「活的；充滿活力的」。*Animated*.（要有活力。）（= *Be animated*. = *Be active*.）可説成：Have an *animated* personality.（要有充滿活力的個性。）Be an *animated* person.（要做一個有活力的人。）（= *Be an active person*.）背 animated 這個字，可先背 animal（動物），「動物」都是「有活力的」。*Artistic*. 在此指 Be *artistic*. 而 artistic 的主要意思是「藝術的」，可作「有藝術鑑賞力的」或「有藝術天賦的」解。當你看到一個人很會畫畫，你可以説：You're very *artistic*.（你很有藝術天賦。）Be *artistic*.（要懂得欣賞藝術。）如懂得欣賞圖畫、攝影、雕刻、電影、戲劇、舞蹈等。

*Seek adventure*.（要尋求冒險。）（= *Seek an unusual or exciting experience*.）*Seek adventure* by traveling abroad.（到國外旅遊尋求冒險。）Be a person who *seeks adventure*.（要做一個有冒險精神的人。）*Amusement*. 在此指 Seek *amusement*.（要尋求娛樂。）（= *Seek entertainment*.）Seek *amusement* through recreation.（要藉由娛樂尋求樂趣。）Spend some time on *amusements*.（要花一些時間在娛樂上。）amusement 可作「娛樂；樂趣」解。*Go abroad*. 可説成：Don't pass up a chance to *go abroad*.（不要錯過出國的機會。）【*pass up* 錯過】

## II. 英語演講：

### 【一字英語演講】　【短篇英語演講】

| 【一字英語演講】 | 【短篇英語演講】 |
|---|---|
| *Greetings, everybody!* | *Greetings, everybody!* 大家好！ |
| | Always be *advancing*. 永遠要進步。 |
| *Advance.* | *Attain* your goals. 要達到你的目標。 |
| *Attain.* | *Acquire* valuable knowledge. 要獲得有價值的知識。 |
| *Acquire.* | |
| | *Be alive* and ready for action. |
| *Be alive.* | 要有活力，隨時準備行動。 |
| *Animated.* | Be an *animated* person. 要做一個有活力的人。 |
| *Artistic.* | Desire to be *artistic*. 要渴望有藝術鑑賞力。 |
| | Be a person who *seeks adventure*. |
| *Seek adventure.* | 要做一個有冒險精神的人。 |
| *Amusement.* | Seek *amusement* through recreation. |
| *Go abroad.* | 要藉由娛樂尋求樂趣。 |
| | Plan a trip to *go abroad*. 要計劃一次出國旅遊。 |
| *That's how to be happy.* | *That's how to be happy.* |
| | 這就是如何才能快樂的方法。 |

## III. 短篇作文：

### How to Be Happy

If you want to be happy, here are some tips. *First*, find a way to *advance* your knowledge. Get pleasure from *attaining* a goal. *Acquire* fluency in a foreign language. *On top of that*, *be alive* and alert. Have an *animated* personality. Desire to be *artistic*. *Likewise*, *seek adventure* through travel. Spend some time on *amusements*. *And finally*, don't pass up a chance to *go abroad*. That's how to bc happy.

**A**

## 如何才能快樂

　　如果你想要快樂，這裡有一些祕訣。第一，要找到能增加知識的方法。要從達到目標中獲得快樂。外語要能說得流利。此外，要有活力又有警覺。要有充滿活力的個性。要渴望有藝術鑑賞力。同樣地，要藉由旅行尋求冒險。花一些時間在娛樂上。最後，不要錯過出國的機會。這就是如何快樂的方法。

> \* tip〔tɪp〕*n.* 祕訣　　fluency〔ˈfluənsɪ〕*n.* 流利
> alert〔əˈlɜt〕*adj.* 警覺的

## IV. 填空：

　　To begin with, always be ___1___ and improving.  Be determined to ___2___ your goals.  Be hungry to ___3___ valuable knowledge.

　　Additionally, be ___4___ and ready for action.  Be an ___5___ and colorful person.  Desire to be ___6___.

　　Finally, be a person who seeks ___7___.  Seek ___8___ through recreation.  Finally, plan a trip to go ___9___ and you'll be happy.

　　首先，永遠要進步。要決心達到目標。要渴望獲得珍貴的知識。

　　此外，要有活力，隨時準備行動。要做一個有活力，而且有趣的人。要渴望有藝術鑑賞力。

　　最後，要做一個有冒險精神的人。要藉由娛樂尋求樂趣。最後，要計劃一次出國旅遊，那樣你就會快樂。

**【解答】** 1. advancing　2. attain　3. acquire　4. alive
　　　　5. animated　6. artistic　7. adventure　8. amusement
　　　　9. abroad

> \* determined〔dɪˈtɜmɪnd〕*adj.* 有決心的
> hungry〔ˈhʌŋgrɪ〕*adj.* 渴望的
> colorful〔ˈkʌləfəl〕*adj.* 多彩多姿的；引人注目的；有趣的
> recreation〔ˌrɛkrɪˈeʃən〕*n.* 娛樂

## V. 詞彙題：

***Directions:*** *Choose the one word that best completes the sentence.*

1. Seize every opportunity to _____ your knowledge.
   (A) abandon　(B) advance　(C) appear　(D) annoy

2. Find joy in _____ what you thought was an impossible goal.
   (A) arresting　(B) absorbing　(C) appealing　(D) attaining

3. Happiness comes when you _____ knowledge and experience.
   (A) acquire　(B) arouse　(C) argue　(D) alter

4. Be the kind of person who is simply happy to be _____.
   (A) annual　(B) absurd　(C) alive　(D) apparent

5. A person with an _____ personality is always fun to be around.
   (A) anonymous　(B) artificial　(C) absolute　(D) animated

6. Be _____ and see the true beauty in everything around you.
   (A) artistic　(B) awkward　(C) allergic　(D) ashamed

7. There is nothing like an _____ to make life interesting.
   (A) application　(B) adventure　(C) agenda　(D) ambulance

8. Without some kind of _____, the daily routine can be kind
   of boring.
   (A) assessment　(B) announcement　(C) amusement
   (D) attachment

9. Everybody should spend some time traveling _____.
   (A) apart　(B) abroad　(C) aside　(D) astray

【答案】1.（B）　2.（D）　3.（A）　4.（C）　5.（D）　6.（A）
　　　　7.（B）　8.（C）　9.（B）

**A**

# VI. 同義字整理：

1. **advance** 〔 əd'væns 〕 v. 前進；
進步

$$\begin{cases} = \text{grow} \ ( \text{gro} ) \\ = \text{upgrade} \ ( \text{'} \text{\textLambda} \text{p'gred} ) \\ = \text{improve} \ ( \text{ɪm'pruv} ) \\ = \text{progress} \ ( \text{prə'grɛs} ) \end{cases}$$

2. **attain** 〔 ə'ten 〕 v. 達到

$$\begin{cases} = \text{reach} \ ( \text{ritʃ} ) \\ = \text{achieve} \ ( \text{ə'tʃiv} ) \\ = \text{obtain} \ ( \text{əb'ten} ) \\ = \text{accomplish} \ ( \text{ə'kɑmplɪʃ} ) \end{cases}$$

3. **acquire** 〔 ə'kwaɪr 〕 v. 獲得

$$\begin{cases} = \text{get} \ ( \text{gɛt} ) \\ = \text{achieve} \ ( \text{ə'tʃiv} ) \\ = \text{earn} \ ( \text{ɝn} ) \end{cases}$$

4. **alive** 〔 ə'laɪv 〕 adj. 活的；充滿
活力的

$$\begin{cases} = \text{lively} \ ( \text{'laɪvlɪ} ) \\ = \text{active} \ ( \text{'æktɪv} ) \\ = \text{energetic} \ ( \text{,ɛnɚ'dʒɛtɪk} ) \end{cases}$$

$$\begin{cases} = \text{animated} \ ( \text{'ænə,metɪd} ) \\ = \text{full of life} \end{cases}$$

5. **animated** 〔 'ænə,metɪd 〕 adj.
有活力的

$$\begin{cases} = \text{lively} \ ( \text{'laɪvlɪ} ) \\ = \text{spirited} \ ( \text{'spɪrɪtɪd} ) \\ = \text{dynamic} \ ( \text{daɪ'næmɪk} ) \\ = \text{energetic} \ ( \text{,ɛnɚ'dʒɛtɪk} ) \end{cases}$$

6. **artistic** 〔 ɑr'tɪstɪk 〕 adj. 藝術的；
有藝術鑑賞力的

$$\begin{cases} = \text{refined} \ ( \text{rɪ'faɪnd} ) \\ = \text{cultured} \ ( \text{'k\textLambda ltʃɚd} ) \\ = \text{sophisticated} \ ( \text{sə'fɪstɪ,ketɪd} ) \\ = \text{aesthetic} \ ( \text{ɛs'θɛtɪk} ) \end{cases}$$

7. **adventure** 〔 əd'vɛntʃɚ 〕 n. 冒險

$$\begin{cases} = \text{experience} \ ( \text{ɪk'spɪrɪəns} ) \\ = \text{excitement} \ ( \text{ɪk'saɪtmənt} ) \\ = \text{venture} \ ( \text{'vɛntʃɚ} ) \end{cases}$$

8. **amusement** 〔 ə'mjuzmənt 〕 n.
娛樂；樂趣

$$\begin{cases} = \text{recreation} \ ( \text{,rɛkrɪ'eʃən} ) \\ = \text{entertainment} \ ( \text{,ɛntɚ'tenmənt} ) \end{cases}$$

$$\begin{cases} = \text{fun} \ ( \text{f\textLambda n} ) \\ = \text{pleasure} \ ( \text{'plɛʒɚ} ) \\ = \text{enjoyment} \ ( \text{ɪn'dʒɔɪmənt} ) \end{cases}$$

9. **abroad** 〔 ə'brɔd 〕 adv. 到國外

$$\begin{cases} = \text{overseas} \ ( \text{'ovɚ'siz} ) \\ = \text{in foreign lands} \\ = \text{not in } \textit{one's} \text{ country} \end{cases}$$

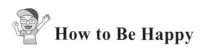 **How to Be Happy**

# *2.* B

B

| 看英文唸出中文 | 一口氣說九句 | 看中文唸出英文 |
|---|---|---|
| **brave**[1]<br>〔 brev 〕*adj.* | Be *brave*.<br>要勇敢。 | 勇敢的 |
| **busy**[1]<br>〔 'bɪzɪ 〕*adj.* | 忙完後洗澡 { *Busy*.<br>要忙碌。 | 忙碌的 |
| **bath**[1]<br>〔 bæθ 〕*n.* | Take a *bath*.<br>要洗澡。 | 洗澡 |

---

| 看英文唸出中文 | 一口氣說九句 | 看中文唸出英文 |
|---|---|---|
| **barefoot**[5]<br>〔 'bɛr͵fʊt 〕*adj., adv.* | 句意相關 { Go *barefoot*.<br>要光著腳走路。 | 光著腳（的） |
| **beach**[1]<br>〔 bitʃ 〕*n.* | To the *beach*.<br>要去海灘。 | 海灘 |
| **breeze**[3]<br>〔 briz 〕*n.* | Enjoy the *breeze*.<br>要享受微風。 | 微風 |

---

| 看英文唸出中文 | 一口氣說九句 | 看中文唸出英文 |
|---|---|---|
| **baseball**[1]<br>〔 'bes͵bɔl 〕*n.* | 三種球類運動 { Play *baseball*.<br>要打棒球。 | 棒球 |
| **basketball**[1]<br>〔 'bæskɪt͵bɔl 〕*n.* | *Basketball*.<br>要打籃球。 | 籃球 |
| **badminton**[2]<br>〔 'bædmɪntən 〕*n.* | *Badminton*.<br>要打羽毛球。 | 羽毛球 |

## I. 背景說明：

*Be brave*.（要勇敢。）（= *Have courage.*）*Be a brave* person.（要做一個勇敢的人。）*Be brave* enough to face any challenge.（要勇敢面對任何挑戰。）*Busy*. 在此指 Be *busy*.（要忙碌。）（= *Be active.*）Stay *busy*.（要保持忙碌。）Keep yourself *busy*.（要使自己保持忙碌。）*Take a bath*. 可說成：*Take a* bubble *bath*.（要洗個泡泡浴。）Enjoy a long hot *bath*.（要享受長時間泡熱水澡的樂趣。）泡熱水澡會使自己身體健康，心情愉快。

*Go barefoot*.（要光著腳走路。）（= *Go without shoes.*）Walk *barefoot* in the grass.（要在草地上光著腳走路。）Take a *barefoot* walk on the beach.（要去海灘光著腳散步。）*To the beach*. 在此指 Go *to the beach*.（要去海灘。）Spend a day at the *beach*.（要在海灘上度過一天。）Invite your friends *to the beach*.（要邀請你的朋友去海灘。）*Enjoy the breeze*. 可說成：Go outside and *enjoy the breeze*.（要去外面享受微風。）*Enjoy the* warm *breeze* on your face.（要享受在你臉上溫暖的微風。）

*Play baseball*.（要打棒球。）不可說成：*Play the baseball*.（誤）或 *Play a baseball*.（誤）*Play baseball* with your friends.（要和你的朋友打棒球。）*Play* a game of *baseball*.（要進行一場棒球比賽。）*Basketball*. 在此指 Play *basketball*.（要打籃球。）「play + 運動名稱」，不得有冠詞。Play *basketball* with your friends.（要和你的朋友打籃球。）Join the *basketball* team at school.（在學校要參加籃球隊。）*Badminton*. 在此指 Play *badminton*.（要打羽毛球。）Learn how to play *badminton*.（要學習如何打羽毛球。）Join a *badminton* club.（要參加羽毛球社。）【club〔klʌb〕*n.* 俱樂部；社團】

## II. 英語演講：

### 【一字英語演講】

*Ladies and gentlemen:*

*Be brave.*
*Busy.*
*Take a bath.*

*Go barefoot.*
*To the beach.*
*Enjoy the breeze.*

*Play baseball.*
*Basketball.*
*Badminton.*

*Follow this path to happiness.*

### 【短篇英語演講】

*Ladies and gentlemen:* 各位先生，各位女士：

*Be* a *brave* person. 要做一個勇敢的人。
Stay *busy*. 要保持忙碌。
*Take a* bubble *bath*. 要洗個泡泡浴。

*Go* walking *barefoot* in the grass.
去草地上光著腳走路。
Invite your friends *to the beach*.
要邀請你的朋友去海灘。
Go outside and *enjoy the breeze*. 要去外面享受微風。

*Play baseball* with your friends.
要和你的朋友打棒球。
Join the *basketball* team at school.
在學校要參加籃球隊。
Learn how to play *badminton*.
要學習如何打羽毛球。

*Follow this path to happiness*. 要遵循這個快樂之道。

## III. 短篇作文：

### The True Path to Happiness

Imagine that happiness is a place and you don't know how to get there. Here are some directions. *To begin with*, *be brave* enough to face any challenge. Keep yourself *busy*. *On the other hand*, *take a* relaxing bubble *bath*. Take a *barefoot* walk on the *beach*. *Enjoy the* warm *breeze* on your face. *After that*, *play* a game of *baseball*. Play *basketball* with your friends. Join a *badminton* club. Follow this path to happiness.

### 眞正的快樂之道

　　想像一下，快樂是個你不知道如何到達的地方。以下有一些方向指引。首先，要勇敢面對任何挑戰。要使自己保持忙碌。另一方面，要洗個能讓人放鬆的泡泡浴。要在海灘上光著腳散步。要享受在你臉上溫暖的微風。在那之後，要進行一場棒球比賽。要和你的朋友打籃球。要參加羽毛球社。要遵循這個快樂之道。

　　* path 〔 pæθ 〕 n. ( 人生的 ) 道路　　　follow 〔'falo〕 v. 順著…前進

## IV. 填空：

　　First, be a ___1___ and courageous person.　Stay ___2___ with a wide range of activities.　But at the end of a tough day, enjoy a long hot ___3___.

　　Meanwhile, go walking ___4___ in the grass.　Spend a day at the ___5___.　Go outside and enjoy the ___6___.

　　Additionally, you can play ___7___ with your friends.　Join the ___8___ team at school.　Maybe learn how to play ___9___.

　　首先，要做一個非常勇敢的人。要有各種活動讓自己忙碌。但在辛苦的一天的最後，要享受長時間泡熱水澡的樂趣。

　　同時，要去草地上光著腳走路。要在海灘上度過一天。要去外面享受微風。

　　此外，你可以和你的朋友打棒球。在學校要參加籃球隊。也許要學習如何打羽毛球。

【解答】 1. brave　2. busy　3. bath　4. barefoot　5. beach
　　　　　 6. breeze　7. baseball　8. basketball　9. badminton
　　　　* courageous 〔 kə'redʒəs 〕 adj. 有勇氣的
　　　　　range 〔 rendʒ 〕 n. 範圍
　　　　　*a wide range of* 範圍廣泛的；各種的

## V. 詞彙題：

***Directions:*** *Choose the one word that best completes the sentence.*

B

1. Sometimes you have to be _____ enough to face your fear.
   (A) brisk   (B) broad   (C) beneficial   (D) brave

2. Time flies when you're _____.
   (A) blank   (B) bloody   (C) busy   (D) basic

3. There's nothing like a nice hot _____ after a long day at work.
   (A) bazaar   (B) bath   (C) banquet   (D) banner

4. I love the feeling of walking _____ on freshly-cut grass.
   (A) barefoot   (B) brilliant   (C) blunt   (D) bizarre

5. What better place to spend a sunny day than the _____?
   (A) branch   (B) bunch   (C) brooch   (D) beach

6. Ah, there's a nice cool _____ coming off the lake today.
   (A) blessing   (B) breeze   (C) blossom   (D) broom

7. Our company gave us free tickets to a _____ game.
   (A) base   (B) basin   (C) baseball   (D) basement

8 My favorite sport has always been _____.
   (A) basketball   (B) badge   (C) ballet   (D) backpack

9. I once won a _____ tournament in college.
   (A) bachelor   (B) badminton   (C) balcony   (D) blizzard

【答案】 1.( D )   2.( C )   3.( B )   4.( A )   5.( D )   6.( B )
　　　　 7.( C )   8.( A )   9.( B )

B

## VI. 同義字整理：

1. **brave** 〔 brev 〕 *adj.* 勇敢的
   - = bold 〔 bold 〕
   - = daring 〔'dɛrɪŋ 〕
   - = courageous 〔 kə'redʒəs 〕
   - = fearless 〔'fɪrlɪs 〕

2. **busy** 〔'bɪzɪ 〕 *adj.* 忙碌的
   - = active 〔'æktɪv 〕
   - = diligent 〔'dɪlədʒənt 〕
   - = industrious 〔 ɪn'dʌstrɪəs 〕
   - = hardworking 〔,hard'wɜkɪŋ 〕

3. **bath** 〔 bæθ 〕 *n.* 洗澡
   - = soak 〔 sok 〕
   - = shower 〔'ʃauə 〕
   - = cleaning 〔'klinɪŋ 〕
   - = soaping 〔'sopɪŋ 〕
   - = scrubbing 〔'skrʌbɪŋ 〕

4. **barefoot** 〔'bɛr,fut 〕 *adj.,adv.*
   光著腳（的）
   - = barefooted 〔'bɛr,futɪd 〕
   - = without shoes

5. **beach** 〔 bitʃ 〕 *n.* 海灘
   - = shore 〔 ʃor 〕
   - = coast 〔 kost 〕
   - = seaside 〔'si,saɪd 〕
   - = seashore 〔'si,ʃor 〕

6. **breeze** 〔 briz 〕 *n.* 微風
   - = gale 〔 gel 〕
   - = wind 〔 wɪnd 〕
   - = gust 〔 gʌst 〕
   - = current of air

7. **baseball** 〔'bes,bɔl 〕 *n.* 棒球
   - = a game played with a bat and ball by two opposing teams of nine players, each team playing alternately in the field and at bat, the players at bat having to run a course of four bases laid out in a diamond pattern in order to score

8. **basketball** 〔'bæskɪt,bɔl 〕 *n.* 籃球
   - = a game played on a court by two opposing teams of 5 players; points are scored by throwing the ball through an elevated horizontal hoop

9. **badminton** 〔'bædmɪntən 〕 *n.*
   羽毛球
   - = a game played with rackets and a shuttlecock, which is hit back and forth across a high net

**How to Be Happy**

# *3.* C (1)

| 看英文唸出中文 | 一口氣說九句 | 看中文唸出英文 |
|---|---|---|

**cheerful**[3]
〔ˈtʃɪrfəl 〕 *adj.*

**childlike**[2]
〔ˈtʃaɪldˌlaɪk 〕 *adj.*

**colorful**[2]
〔ˈkʌləˌfəl 〕 *adj.*

字首是 ch

Be *cheerful*.
要愉快。

*Childlike*.
要像小孩一樣純眞。

Very *colorful*.
要非常多彩多姿。

愉快的

純眞的

多彩多姿的

---

**curious**[2]
〔ˈkjʊrɪəs 〕 *adj.*

**courteous**[4]
〔ˈkɝtɪəs 〕 *adj.*

**courageous**[4]
〔 kəˈredʒəs 〕 *adj.*

字首是 cour

Truly *curious*.
要眞的很好奇。

Extremely
*courteous*.
要非常有禮貌。

Exceptionally
*courageous*.
要特別有勇氣。

字尾是 ous

好奇的

有禮貌的

有勇氣的

---

**charity**[4]
〔ˈtʃærətɪ 〕 *n.*

**community**[4]
〔 kəˈmjunətɪ 〕 *n.*

**companionship**[6]
〔kəmˈpænjənˌʃɪp 〕 *n.*

字首是 Com

Seek *charity*.
要找機會做善事。

*Community*.
要融入社區。

*Companionship*.
要尋求友誼。

字尾是 ity

慈善

社區

友誼

# I. 背景説明：

*Be cheerful.* ( = *Be a cheerful person.* ) Have a *cheerful* personality. ( 要有愉快的個性。) Surround yourself with *cheerful* people. ( 你周圍要有高高興興的人。) *Childlike.* 在此指 Be *childlike.* ( 要像小孩一樣純眞。) Have a *childlike* personality. ( 要有純眞的個性。) Be *childlike* and full of wonder. ( 要像小孩一樣純眞，充滿好奇。) ( = *Be childlike and full of curiosity.* ) *Very colorful.* 在此指 Be *very colorful.* ( 要非常多彩多姿。) 也就是「要過著非常多彩多姿的生活。」( = *Live a very colorful life.* ) Be an exceptionally *colorful* person. ( 要做一個非常有趣又充滿活力的人。) ( = *Be a very interesting and dynamic person.* ) 所謂「多彩多姿」，就是「很風趣、有活力、很快樂」(*full of interest, lively and exciting* )。

*Truly curious.* 在此指 Be *truly curious.* ( 要眞的很好奇。) ( = *Be really curious.* = *Be very curious.* ) Be a *truly curious* person. ( 要做一個非常好奇的人。) Have a genuinely *curious* mind. ( 要有眞正的好奇心。) *Extremely courteous.* 在此指 Be *extremely courteous.* ( 要非常有禮貌。) ( = *Be well-mannered and polite.* ) Be *extremely courteous* to others. ( 對他人要非常有禮貌。) Be a very *courteous* person. ( 要做一個非常有禮貌的人。) courteous 源自 court ( 宮廷 )，在宮廷裡的每一個人都非常有禮貌。*Exceptionally courageous.* 在此指 Be *exceptionally courageous*.（要特別有勇氣。）（ *= Be extra brave.* ）Have an *exceptionally courageous* attitude.（要有非常勇敢的態度。）Be an unusually *courageous* person.（要做一個非常有勇氣的人。）中文裡的「非常」，不是常態，所以英文用 unusually，exceptionally 來表示。

charity 的意思是「慈悲；仁愛；慈善；善舉；做好事」。*Seek charity*. 的意思是「尋找做好事的機會。」也就是「要找機會做善事。」（ *= Seek opportunities to be kind.* ）Donate your time to *charity*.（要奉獻你的時間做善事。）Give money to *charity*.（要捐錢做善事。）*Community*. 在此是指 Seek *community*.（要努力成為社區的一份子。）（ *= Seek to be a part of the community.* ）在社區裡，要跟左鄰右舍交往才會快樂。Join the *community*.（要參與社區的活動。）所謂 community，有大有小，如住在一棟建築物中，整棟建築物就是一個社區，也可能包含周圍的鄰居。Seek *community*. 的意思是「要融入社區。」不是坐在家裡面，而是出去和你的鄰居交往，了解你的社區。（ Don't sit at home.  Go out and mingle with your neighbors.  Spend time getting to know your community. ）*Companionship*. 在此指 Seek *companionship*.（要尋求友誼。）（ *= Seek friendship.* ）友誼是要自己尋找的，朋友越多越快樂。Seek the *companionship* of others.（要尋求和他人的友誼。）*Companionship* is a priceless gift.（友誼是無價的禮物。）

## II. 英語演講：

| 【一字英語演講】 | 【短篇英語演講】 |
|---|---|

**Students and parents:**

**Be cheerful.**
**Childlike.**
**Very colorful.**

**Truly curious.**
**Extremely courteous.**
**Exceptionally courageous.**

**Seek charity.**
**Community.**
**Companionship.**

**These are great ways to be happy.**

---

***Students and parents:*** 各位同學和家長：

Have a *cheerful* personality.　要有愉快的個性。
Be *childlike* and full of wonder.
要像小孩一樣純眞，充滿好奇。
Live a *very colorful* life.
要過著非常多彩多姿的生活。

Be a *truly curious* person.　要做一個非常好奇的人。
Be *extremely courteous* to others.
對他人要非常有禮貌。
Be an *exceptionally courageous* person.
要做一個非常有勇氣的人。

Donate your time to *charity*.
要奉獻你的時間做善事。
Join the *community*.　要參加社區的活動。
Seek the *companionship* of others.
要尋求和他人的友誼。

***These are great ways to be happy*.**
這些是要快樂的絕佳方法。

## III. 短篇作文：

### Great Ways to Be Happy

　　There are a bunch of great ways to be happy.　*First of all*, surround yourself with *cheerful* people.　Have a *childlike* personality. Live a very *colorful* life.　*Likewise*, have a truly *curious* mind.　Be an *extremely courteous* person.　Have an *exceptionally courageous* attitude.　*Moreover*, give money to *charity*.　Spend time getting to know your *community*.　*And finally*, remember that *companionship* is a priceless gift.

### 要快樂的絕佳方法

　　有許多絕佳的方法能讓人快樂。首先,你周圍要有高高興興的人。要有純真的個性。要過著非常多彩多姿的生活。同樣地,要有真正的好奇心。要做一個非常有禮貌的人。要有非常勇敢的態度。此外,捐錢做善事。要花時間了解你的社區。最後,要記得,友誼是無價的禮物。

* surround〔sə'raʊnd〕*v.* 使環繞　　***a bunch of*** 許多的;大量的
***get to V.*** 得以…　　priceless〔'praɪslɪs〕*adj.* 無價的

C

## IV. 填空:

　　In the first place, have a ___1___ personality.　Be ___2___ and full of wonder.　Live a very ___3___ life.

　　Meanwhile, be a truly ___4___ person.　Be extremely ___5___ to others.　Be an unusually ___6___ person.

　　Additionally, donate your time to ___7___.　Join your local ___8___.　And the best way to be happy is to seek the ___9___ of others.

　　首先,要有愉快的個性。要像小孩一樣純真,充滿好奇。要過著非常多彩多姿的生活。

　　同時,要做一個非常好奇的人。對他人要非常有禮貌。要做一個非常有勇氣的人。

　　此外,要奉獻你的時間做善事。要參與當地社區的活動。而且要快樂最好的方式,就是尋求和他人的友誼。

【解答】 1. cheerful　　2. childlike　　3. colorful　　4. curious
　　　　　5. courteous　6. courageous　7. charity
　　　　　8. community　9. companionship

* wonder〔'wʌndɚ〕*n.* 驚奇　　donate〔'donet〕*v.* 捐贈
local〔'lokḷ〕*adj.* 當地的

## V. 詞彙題：

***Directions:*** *Choose the one word that best completes the sentence.*

1. _____ people brighten any room they enter.
   (A) Classical   (B) Chilly   (C) Cheerful   (D) Chronic

2. Go through life with a _____ sense of wonder.
   (A) childlike   (B) capable   (C) chemical   (D) clumsy

3. Why be dull and boring when you could be a _____ character?
   (A) commercial   (B) colorful   (C) clear   (D) civil

4. Never stop being _____ about the world around you.
   (A) chief   (B) cloudy   (C) curious   (D) circular

5. People will be impressed by your _____ manner.
   (A) central   (B) chubby   (C) clinical   (D) courteous

6. Be _____ in the face of danger.
   (A) courageous   (B) cunning   (C) complex   (D) compact

7. Set aside a certain portion of your income to give to _____.
   (A) capacity   (B) charity   (C) clarity   (D) category

8. Be a leader within your _____.
   (A) complexity   (B) continuity   (C) curiosity   (D) community

9. No one values _____ more than a lonely person.
   (A) criticism   (B) contrast   (C) companionship
   (D) consensus

【答案】 1.（C）　2.（A）　3.（B）　4.（C）　5.（D）　6.（A）
　　　　 7.（B）　8.（D）　9.（C）

## VI. 同義字整理：

**1. cheerful**〔'tʃɪrfəl〕 *adj.* 愉快的
- = happy〔'hæpɪ〕
- = glad〔glæd〕
- = joyful〔'dʒɔɪfəl〕

**2. childlike**〔'tʃaɪld,laɪk〕 *adj.* 純眞的
- = naive〔nɑ'iv〕
- = simple〔'sɪmpļ〕
- = trusting〔'trʌstɪŋ〕
- = innocent〔'ɪnəsṇt〕

**3. colorful**〔'kʌləfəl〕 *adj.* 多彩多姿的；很風趣的；有活力的
- = bright〔braɪt〕
- = vivid〔'vɪvɪd〕
- = rich〔rɪtʃ〕
- = dynamic〔daɪ'næmɪk〕

**4. curious**〔'kjʊrɪəs〕 *adj.* 好奇的
- = inquisitive〔ɪn'kwɪzətɪv〕
- = questioning〔'kwɛstʃənɪŋ〕
- = searching〔'sɝtʃɪŋ〕
- = inquiring〔ɪn'kwaɪrɪŋ〕

**5. courteous**〔'kɝtɪəs〕 *adj.* 有禮貌的
- = civil〔'sɪvļ〕
- = polite〔pə'laɪt〕
- = gracious〔'greʃəs〕
- = well-mannered〔'wɛl'mænəd〕

**6. courageous**〔kə'redʒəs〕 *adj.* 有勇氣的
- = brave〔brev〕
- = daring〔'dɛrɪŋ〕
- = bold〔bold〕

- = fearless〔'fɪrlɪs〕
- = valiant〔'væljənt〕

**7. charity**〔'tʃærətɪ〕 *n.* 慈善；慈善機構
- ① = donations〔do'neʃənz〕
  - = contributions〔ˌkɑntrə'bjuʃənz〕
- ② = charitable organization

**8. community**〔kə'mjunətɪ〕 *n.* 社區
- = group〔grup〕
- = area〔'ɛrɪə〕
- = district〔'dɪstrɪkt〕
- = society〔sə'saɪətɪ〕

**9. companionship**〔kəm'pænjən,ʃɪp〕 *n.* 友誼
- = fellowship〔'fɛloʃɪp〕
- = friendship〔'frɛndʃɪp〕

C

## How to Be Happy

# *4.* C (2)

| 看英文唸出中文 | 一口氣說九句 | 看中文唸出英文 |
|---|---|---|
| **content**[5]<br>〔kən'tɛnt〕*adj.* | Be really *content*.<br>要真的知足。 | 滿足的 |
| **compassionate**[5]<br>〔kəm'pæʃənɪt〕*adj.* | Very *compassionate*.<br>要非常有同情心。 | 同情的 |
| **conscientious**[6]<br>〔͵kɑnʃɪ'ɛnʃəs〕*adj.* | Deeply *conscientious*.<br>要很有良心。 | 有良心的 |

字首是 CO

| | | |
|---|---|---|
| **charitable**[6]<br>〔'tʃærətəbḷ〕*adj.* | *Charitable*.<br>要有善心。 | 慈善的 |
| **cooperative**[4]<br>〔ko'ɑpə͵retɪv〕*adj.* | *Cooperative*.<br>要合作。 | 合作的 |
| **carefree**[5]<br>〔'kɛr͵fri〕*adj.* | Truly *carefree*.<br>要真的無憂無慮。 | 無憂無慮的 |

句意相關

| | | |
|---|---|---|
| **celebrate**[3]<br>〔'sɛlə͵bret〕*v.* | *Celebrate* life.<br>要歌頌生命。 | 慶祝;歌頌 |
| **conversation**[2]<br>〔͵kɑnvɚ'seʃən〕*n.* | Join the *conversation*.<br>要參與對話。 | 對話 |
| **contribution**[4]<br>〔͵kɑntrə'bjuʃən〕*n.* | Make a *contribution*.<br>要有貢獻。 | 貢獻 |

句意相關

C

## I. 背景說明：

*Be really content.*（要真的知足。）(*= Be happy, not greedy.*)
快樂、不貪心，就是「知足」。Be a *content* person.（要做一個知足
的人。）Be *content* with what you have.（要滿足於你所擁有的。）
*Very compassionate.* 在此指 Be *very compassionate*.（要非常有
同情心。）Be a *compassionate* person.（要做一個有同情心的人。）
Treat others *very compassionately*.（對別人要非常有同情心。）
*Deeply conscientious.* 在此指 Be *deeply conscientious*.（要很有
良心。）Be a *conscientious* and honorable person.（要做一個有
良心，值得尊敬的人。）Be a genuinely *conscientious* person.
（要做一個真正有良心的人。）由於 content, compassionate,
conscientious 在 How to Be Popular（人見人愛經）中出現過，
所以我們加上副詞，背到變成直覺時，才不會和另一篇混淆。有
了這些副詞，會使你的口才更好。

這六個副詞都可和後面的形容詞搭配，不是每個副詞都可以。如：

　　*Be deeply content.*【誤，文法對，但美國人不說】
　　Be deeply conscientious.【正】

**C**

*Charitable.* 在此指 Be *charitable.*（要有善心。）Be a very *charitable* person.（要做一個非常有善心的人。）Be *charitable* and generous.（要有善心並慷慨。）*Cooperative.* 在此指 Be *cooperative.*（要合作。）Seek *cooperative* opportunities.（要尋找合作的機會。）Have a *cooperative* attitude.（要有合作的態度。）*Truly carefree.* 在此指 Be *truly carefree.*（要真的無憂無慮。）( = *Be truly free from worry.* ) Be a *truly carefree* individual.（要做一個真正無憂無慮的人。）Be a happy-go-lucky and *carefree* person.（要做一個隨遇而安，無憂無慮的人。）

*Celebrate life.* ( = *Express your love of life; be happy to be alive.* ) Be a person who *celebrates life.*（要做一個歌頌生命的人。）*Celebrate life* with positive experiences.（要以正面的經驗來歌頌生命。）celebrate 的意思有：①慶祝②讚揚；歌頌。*Join the conversation.* 可說成：Be eager to *join* any *conversation.*（要渴望加入任何的對話。）Participate in the *conversation.*（要參與對話。）*Make a contribution.* 可加強語氣說成：*Make a* significant *contribution.*（要做有意義的貢獻。）Always *make a contribution* to the conversation.（一定要對談話有貢獻。）你要快樂，就要在交談時，把自己的想法和意見貢獻給別人。

## II. 英語演講：

### 【一字英語演講】

*Greetings, all:*

*Be really content.*
*Very compassionate.*
*Deeply*
*   conscientious.*

*Charitable.*
*Cooperative.*
*Truly carefree.*

*Celebrate life.*
*Join the*
*   conversation.*
*Make a*
*   contribution.*

*These are easy ways*
*   to be happy.*

### 【短篇英語演講】

*Greetings, all:* 大家好：

*Be really content* with what you have.
要對於你所擁有的非常滿足。
Be a *compassionate* person.
要做一個有同情心的人。
Be a *deeply conscientious* and honorable person.
要做一個非常有良心，值得尊敬的人。

Be *charitable* and generous. 要有善心並慷慨。
Have a *cooperative* attitude. 要有合作的態度。
Be a *truly carefree* individual.
要做一個真正無憂無慮的人。

*Celebrate life* with positive experiences.
要以正面的經驗來歌頌生命。
Be eager to *join* any *conversation*.
要渴望加入任何的對話。
Always *make a contribution* to the conversation.
一定要對談話有貢獻。

*These are easy ways to be happy*.
這些就是要快樂的簡易方法。

## III. 短篇作文：

### Easy Ways to Be Happy

Happiness is an elusive state of mind, but there are some easy ways to be happy. *To begin with*, be a *content* person. Treat others *very compassionately*. Be a genuinely *conscientious* person. *Additionally*, be a very *charitable* person. Seek *cooperative* opportunities. Be a happy-go-lucky and *carefree* person. *What's more*, *celebrate life* with positive experiences. Participate in the *conversation*. *However*, the easiest way to be happy is to *make a* significant *contribution* to whatever you're doing.

### 要快樂的簡易方法

快樂是一種難以捉摸的心理狀態，但要快樂，有一些簡易的方法。首先，要做一個知足的人。對別人要非常有同情心。要做一個眞正有良心的人。此外，要做一個非常有善心的人。要尋找合作的機會。要做一個隨遇而安，無憂無慮的人。而且，要以正面的經驗來歌頌生命。要參與對話。然而，要快樂最簡單的方法，就是要對你所做的任何事做有意義的貢獻。

> \* elusive〔ɪ'lusɪv〕*adj.* 難懂的；無法捉摸的
> genuinely〔'dʒɛnjʊɪnlɪ〕*adv.* 眞正地
> positive〔'pɑzətɪv〕*adj.* 正面的
> significant〔sɪg'nɪfəkənt〕*adj.* 意義重大的

## IV. 填空：

First of all, be ___1___ with what you have.  Be a ___2___ person.  Be a ___3___ and honorable person.

On top of that, be ___4___ and generous.  Have a ___5___ attitude.  Be a truly ___6___ individual.

Finally, be a person who ___7___ life.  Be eager to join any ___8___.  Always make a ___9___ to the conversation.

首先，要滿足於你所擁有的。要做一個有同情心的人。要做一個有良心，值得尊敬的人。

此外，要有善心並慷慨。要有合作的態度。要做一個眞正無憂無慮的人。

最後，要做一個歌頌生命的人。要渴望加入任何的對話。一定要對談話有貢獻。

【解答】 1. content　2. compassionate　3. conscientious
4. charitable　5. cooperative　6. carefree
7. celebrates　8. conversation　9. contribution

## V. 詞彙題：

***Directions:*** *Choose the one word that best completes the sentence.*

1. The happiest people are _____ with what they have.
   (A) constructive  (B) constitutional  C) constant  (D) content

2. The world needs more _____ people who care about others.
   (A) comparative  (B) compassionate  (C) complete
   (D) comparable

3. Be a _____ person and never worry about making a mistake.
   (A) conscientious  (B) continuous  (C) concrete  (D) concise

4. A good feeling will come when you make a _____ donation.
   (A) compatible  (B) comfortable  (C) charitable
   (D) countable

5. You will accomplish a lot more with a _____ attitude.
   (A) cooperative  (B) contrary  (C) continental  (D) costly

6. A _____ person does not carry the weight of the world.
   (A) convenient  (B) credible  (C) controversial  (D) carefree

7. Every now and then, it's important to _____.
   (A) confuse  (B) collapse  (C) celebrate  (D) circulate

8. Nothing is more important than good _____.
   (A) collision  (B) conversation  (C) corruption
   (D) confrontation

9. Make your best _____ and let the chips fall where they may.
   (A) caution  (B) confusion  (C) contribution  (D) collection

【答案】1.（D）  2.（B）  3.（A）  4.（C）  5.（A）  6.（D）
　　　　7.（C）  8.（B）  9.（C）

# VI. 同義字整理：

**1. content** 〔 kən'tɛnt 〕 *adj.* 滿足的

- = happy 〔'hæpɪ 〕
- = pleased 〔 plizd 〕
- = satisfied 〔'sætɪs,faɪd 〕
- = contented 〔 kən'tɛntɪd 〕

**2. compassionate**
〔 kəm'pæʃənɪt 〕 *adj.* 同情的

- = sympathetic 〔,sɪmpə'θɛtɪk 〕
- = understanding 〔,ʌndə'stændɪŋ 〕
- = humanitarian 〔 hju,mænə'tɛrɪən 〕

**3. conscientious** 〔,kɑnʃɪ'ɛnʃəs 〕
*adj.* 有良心的

- = moral 〔'mɔrəl 〕
- = upright 〔'ʌp,raɪt 〕
- = honest 〔'ɑnɪst 〕
- = honorable 〔'ɑnərəbḷ 〕

**4. charitable** 〔'tʃærətəbḷ 〕 *adj.* 慈善的

- = kind 〔 kaɪnd 〕
- = generous 〔'dʒɛnərəs 〕
- = benevolent 〔 bə'nɛvḷənt 〕

**5. cooperative** 〔 ko'ɑpə,retɪv 〕 *adj.*
合作的

- = supportive 〔 sə'portɪv 〕
- = collaborative 〔 kə'læbə,retɪv 〕
- = working together toward
  a common end

**6. carefree** 〔'kɛr,fri 〕 *adj.*
無憂無慮的

- = cheerful 〔'tʃɪrfəl 〕
- = untroubled 〔 ʌn'trʌbḷd 〕
- = easygoing 〔'izɪ,goɪŋ 〕
- = happy-go-lucky
  〔'hæpɪgo'lʌkɪ 〕

**7. celebrate** 〔'sɛlə,bret 〕 *v.*
慶祝；歌頌

- = praise 〔 prez 〕
- = honor 〔'ɑnə 〕
- = commend 〔 kə'mɛnd 〕
- = glorify 〔'glorə,faɪ 〕

**8. conversation**
〔,kɑnvə'seʃən 〕 *n.* 對話

- = talk 〔 tɔk 〕
- = chat 〔 tʃæt 〕
- = exchange 〔 ɪk'stʃendʒ 〕
- = dialogue 〔'daɪə,lɔg 〕

**9. contribution**
〔,kɑntrə'bjuʃən 〕 *n.* 貢獻

- = input 〔'ɪn,pʊt 〕
- = offering 〔'ɔfərɪŋ 〕
- = donation 〔 do'neʃən 〕

C

**How to Be Happy**

# 5. D (1)

| 看英文唸出中文 | 一口氣說九句 | 看中文唸出英文 |
|---|---|---|
| **decent**[6]<br>〔'disn̩t 〕 *adj.* | 字首是de { | Be very ***decent***.<br>要非常正派。 | 高尚的 |
| **decisive**[6]<br>〔 dɪ'saɪsɪv 〕 *adj.* | | ***Decisive***.<br>要果斷。 | 果斷的 |
| **dancer**[1]<br>〔'dænsɚ 〕 *n.* | | A ***dancer***.<br>要會跳舞。 | 舞者 |

| | | |
|---|---|---|
| **date**[1]<br>〔 det 〕 *v. n.* | 句意相關 { | ***Date***.<br>要約會。 | 約會 |
| **dream**[1]<br>〔 drim 〕 *v.* | | ***Dream***.<br>要做夢。 | 做夢 |
| **delight**[4]<br>〔 dɪ'laɪt 〕 *v.* | | ***Delight***.<br>要愉快。 | 愉快 |

| | | |
|---|---|---|
| **dumpling**[2]<br>〔'dʌmplɪŋ 〕 *n.* | 三種食物 { | Eat ***dumplings***.<br>要吃水餃。 | 水餃 |
| **doughnut**[2]<br>〔'do͵nʌt 〕 *n.* | | ***Doughnuts***.<br>要吃甜甜圈。 | 甜甜圈 |
| **duck**[1]<br>〔 dʌk 〕 *n.* | | Peking ***duck***.<br>要吃北京烤鴨。 | 鴨子 |

D

## I. 背景説明：

*Be very decent*. 可説成：*Be a very decent* person. ( 要做一個非常正派的人。) Have a *very decent* and respectable character. ( 要有非常高尚，讓人尊敬的個性。) decent 的意思有：「高尚的；好的；得體的；正派的；適當的；還可以的」，一個英文字往往有無限多的意思，要看前後句意來判斷。*Decisive*. 在此指 Be *decisive*. ( 要果斷。) ( = *Be quick to make a decision*. ) Be a *decisive* person. ( 要做一個果斷的人。) Be confident and *decisive*. ( 要有信心又果斷。) *A dancer*. 在此指 Be *a dancer*. ( 要會跳舞。) Be *a* good *dancer*. ( 要很會跳舞。) Desire to be *a dancer*. ( 要很想跳舞。)

*Date*. ( 要約會。) 約會會讓人快樂。Start *dating* someone. ( 要開始和人約會。) Go on a *date* with your lover. ( 要和你心愛的人約會。) date 和 appointment 不一樣，date 是「( 男女之間的 ) 約會」。

> 【比較】 I have a *date* with Mary.
> ( 我和瑪麗要約會。)
> I have a doctor's *appointment*.
> ( 我和醫生有約。)

*Dream*. 做夢是最讓人快樂的事。所謂「做夢」，就是「運用你的想像力。」(Use your imagination. ) *Dream* big. ( 要做大夢。) *Dream* big dreams. ( 要有遠大的夢想。) *Dream* of the future. ( 要夢想未來。) *Delight*. 可説成：*Delight* in love. ( 要愉快地談戀愛。) *Delight* in travel. ( 要愉快地去旅遊。) *Delight* in work. ( 要樂在工作。) 【*delight in* 喜歡；樂於做…】

　　*Eat dumplings.* 可説成：*Eat* some *dumplings.*（要吃一些水餃。）Make some *dumplings.*（要做一些水餃。）*Doughnuts.* 在此指 Eat *doughnuts.*（要吃甜甜圈。）Buy a box of *doughnuts.*（要買一盒甜甜圈。）Enjoy some *doughnuts.*（要享用一些甜甜圈。）doughnut 可寫成 donut，發音相同。*Peking duck.* 在此指 Eat *Peking duck.*（要吃北京烤鴨。）Have a meal of *Peking duck.*（要吃北京烤鴨餐。）Go to a restaurant that's famous for *Peking duck.*（要去一家以北京烤鴨有名的餐廳。）

**D**

*Boys and girls, ladies and gentlemen:*

Be very decent.
Decisive.
A dancer.

Date.
Dream.
Delight.

Eat dumplings.
Doughnuts.
Peking duck.

*That's how to achieve happiness.*

## II. **短篇英語演講：**

> ***Boys and girls**, **ladies and gentlemen:***
> 各位男孩和女孩，先生和女士：

> ***Be** a **very decent** person.* 要做一個非常正派的人。
> *Be a **decisive** person.* 要做一個果斷的人。
> *Be **a** good **dancer**.* 要很會跳舞。

> *Start **dating** someone.* 要開始和人約會。
> ***Dream** big dreams.* 要有遠大的夢想。
> ***Delight** in love.* 要愉快地談戀愛。

> ***Eat** some **dumplings**.* 要吃一些水餃。
> *Buy a box of **doughnuts**.* 要買一盒甜甜圈。
> *Go to a restaurant that's famous for **Peking duck**.*
> 要去一家以北京烤鴨有名的餐廳。

> ***That's how to achieve happiness**.*
> 那就是如何快樂的方法。

## III. **短篇作文：**

### How to Achieve Happiness

    It might seem like an impossible task, but there are ways to achieve happiness. *First of all*, have a ***very decent*** and respectable character. Be confident and *decisive*. Desire to be *a dancer*. *Besides*, start *dating* someone. ***Dream*** of the future. ***Delight*** in travel. *Next*, *eat* some ***dumplings***. Enjoy some ***doughnuts***. *And finally*, if you really want to achieve happiness, have a meal of ***Peking duck***.

D

### 如何才能快樂

這可能像是個不可能的任務，不過還是有一些方法可以讓人快樂。首先，要有非常高尚、讓人尊敬的個性。要有信心又果斷。要很想跳舞。此外，要開始和人約會。要夢想未來。要愉快地去旅遊。其次，要吃一些水餃。要享用一些甜甜圈。最後，如果你真的想要快樂，就要吃北京烤鴨餐。

## IV. 填空：

First, be a ___1___ person who always does the right thing.  Be a ___2___ person who makes a decision and sticks with it.  Be a good ___3___.

Meanwhile, try ___4___ someone you're attracted to. ___5___ big dreams and reach for the stars.  ___6___ in love.

Finally, eat some ___7___.  Buy a box of ___8___ to share with friends.  Go to a restaurant that's famous for Peking ___9___.

　　首先，要做一個正派的人，總是做正確的事。要做一個果斷的人，能做出決定，並堅持到底。要很會跳舞。

　　同時，要試著和吸引你的人約會。要有遠大的夢想，設定不易達成的目標。要愉快地談戀愛。

　　最後，要吃一些水餃。買一盒甜甜圈和朋友分享。要去一家以北京烤鴨有名的餐廳。

【解答】 1. decent　　2. decisive　　3. dancer　　4. dating
　　　　　5. Dream　　6. Delight　　7. dumplings
　　　　　8. doughnuts　　9. duck

## V. 詞彙題：

***Directions:*** *Choose the one word that best completes the sentence.*

1. It really doesn't take a lot of effort to be a _____ person.
   (A) damp   (B) decent   (C) dense   (D) destined

2. Being a _____ person will pay dividends in the future.
   (A) decisive   (B) deadly   (C) distant   (D) dizzy

3. Being a _____ is a lot of fun and great exercise, too.
   (A) disorder   (B) disaster   (C) dancer   (D) diaper

4. _____ the most attractive person you know.
   (A) Derive   (B) Dwell   (C) Drain   (D) Date

5. There's nothing to stop you from _____ big dreams.
   (A) drowning   (B) dripping   (C) dreaming   (D) dumping

6. _____ in all the small miracles of life.
   (A) Delight   (B) Divide   (C) Divert   (D) Distort

7. Nothing is better than a big plate of fresh _____.
   (A) disasters   (B) dumplings   (C) diplomas   (D) dynamites

8. I could easily eat a whole box of _____ right now.
   (A) dialogues   (B) deadlines   (C) defects   (D) doughnuts

9. Doesn't some Peking _____ sound good right about now?
   (A) dove   (B) dose   (C) duck   (D) disk

【答案】 1.(B)　2.(A)　3.(C)　4.(D)　5.(C)　6.(A)
　　　　　7.(B)　8.(D)　9.(C)

## VI. 同義字整理：

1. **decent** (ˈdisn̩t ) *adj.* 高尚的
   = good ( gʊd )
   = proper (ˈprɑpɚ )
   = respectable ( rɪˈspɛktəbl̩ )
   = courteous (ˈkɝtɪəs )

2. **decisive** ( dɪˈsaɪsɪv ) *adj.* 果斷的
   = firm ( fɝm )
   = forceful (ˈforsfəl )
   = resolute (ˈrɛzə‚lut )
   = determined ( dɪˈtɝmɪnd )

3. **dancer** (ˈdænsɚ ) *n.* 舞者
   = hoofer (ˈhʊfɚ )
   = ballerina (‚bæləˈrinə )
   = a person who dances

4. **date** ( det ) *v.* 約會
   = go out with
   = go around with
   = be romantically involved
     with
   = go steady with

5. **dream** ( drim ) *v.* 做夢；夢想
   = aspire ( əˈspaɪr )
   = reach for the stars
   = set *one's* heart on
   = have a fervent hope or
     aspiration

6. **delight** ( dɪˈlaɪt ) *v.* 愉快；很喜歡
   = like ( laɪk )
   = love ( lʌv )
   = enjoy ( ɪnˈdʒɔɪ )
   = appreciate ( əˈpriʃɪ‚et )
   = indulge in
   = take pleasure in

7. **dumpling** (ˈdʌmplɪŋ ) *n.* 水餃
   = a piece of dough, sometimes
     filled, that is cooked in
     liquid such as water or soup

8. **doughnut** (ˈdo‚nʌt ) *n.* 甜甜圈
   = donut (ˈdo‚nʌt )
   = a small ring-shaped cake
     made of rich, light dough
     that is deep-fried in fat

9. **Peking duck** 北京烤鴨
   = a Chinese dish of roast
     duck with crispy skin,
     often served with thin
     pancakes, scallions, and
     hoisin sauce

**D**

**How to Be Happy**

# 6. D (2)

| 看英文唸出中文 | 一 口 氣 説 九 句 | 看中文唸出英文 |
|---|---|---|
| **dance**[1]<br>〔 dæns 〕 *v.* | ***Dance.***<br>要跳舞。 | 跳舞 |
| **draw**[1]<br>〔 drɔ 〕 *v.* | ***Draw.***<br>要畫畫。 | 畫 |
| **dare**[3]<br>〔 dɛr 〕 *v.* | ***Dare*** to dream.<br>要勇於做夢。 | 敢 |
| **dinner**[1]<br>〔ˈdɪnɚ〕 *n.* | Have ***dinner.***<br>要吃大餐。 | 晚餐；大餐 |
| **dessert**[2]<br>〔 dɪˈzɝt 〕 *n.* | ***Dessert.***<br>要吃甜點。 | 甜點 |
| **delicious**[2]<br>〔 dɪˈlɪʃəs 〕 *adj.* | ***Delicious*** food.<br>要吃美味的食物。 | 美味的 |
| **daydream**[3]<br>〔ˈdeˌdrim〕 *v.* | ***Daydream.***<br>要做白日夢。 | 做白日夢 |
| **DVD**[4] | Watch ***DVDs.***<br>要看 DVD。 | 數位影音光碟 |
| **disco**[3]<br>〔ˈdɪsko〕 *n.* | Go to a ***disco.***<br>去迪斯可舞廳。 | 迪斯可舞廳 |

（都是食物）

## I. 背景説明：

　　跳舞會讓你快樂。*Dance*. 可説成：*Dance* to the music. （要隨著音樂起舞。）注意，介系詞要用 to，不可用 with。*Dance* like no one is watching you. （要旁若無人地跳舞。）*Draw*. 可説成：*Draw* some pictures. （要畫一些圖畫。）Try to *draw* something you see in your mind. （要試著畫你心中看到的東西。）*Dare to dream*. 可説成：*Dare to dream* of being successful. （要勇於夢想成功。）*Dare to dream* of doing something great. （要勇於夢想做大事。）

　　*Have dinner*. 可説成：*Have* a nice *dinner*. （要好好吃一頓。）Treat yourself to a good *dinner*. （要請自己吃一頓大餐。）*Dessert*. 在此指 Have *dessert*. （要吃甜點。）Order some *dessert*. （要點一些甜點。）Have an extra serving of *dessert*. （要再吃一份甜點。）【serving〔ˈsɝvɪŋ〕n. 一份】*Delicious food*. 在此指 Have *delicious food*. （要吃美味的食物。）Treat yourself to *delicious food*. （要招待自己吃美食。）Make some *delicious food*. （要做一些美食。）

　　*Daydream*. 可説成：Spend some time *daydreaming*. （要花一些時間做白日夢。）Don't be afraid to *daydream*. （不要害怕做白日夢。）*Watch DVDs*. 可説成：*Watch* some movies on *DVD*. （要用 DVD 看一些電影。）*Watch* some funny shows on *DVD*. （要用 DVD 看一些有趣的表演。）*Go to a disco*. 可説成：Go dancing at a *disco*. （去迪斯可舞廳跳舞。）*Go to a disco* tonight. （今晚去迪斯可舞廳。）*Go to a* trendy *disco*. （要去一間時髦的迪可斯舞廳。）【trendy〔ˈtrɛndɪ〕adj. 時髦的】

## II. 英語演講：

### 【一字英語演講】

*Dear friends and associates:*

*Dance.*
*Draw.*
*Dare to dream.*

*Have dinner.*
*Dessert.*
*Delicious food.*

*Daydream.*
*Watch DVDs.*
*Go to a disco.*

*Get ready to be happy now!*

### 【短篇英語演講】

*Dear friends and associates:* 親愛的朋友和同事：

*Dance* to the music. 要隨著音樂起舞。
*Draw* some pictures. 要畫一些圖畫。
*Dare to dream* of being successful.
要勇於夢想成功。

*Have* a nice *dinner*. 要好好吃一頓。
Order some *dessert*. 要點一些甜點。
Treat yourself to *delicious food*.
要招待自己吃美食。

Spend some time *daydreaming*.
要花一些時間做白日夢。
*Watch* some movies on *DVD*.
要用 DVD 看一些電影。
*Go* dancing at *a disco*. 去迪斯可舞廳跳舞。

*Get ready to be happy now!*
現在就準備好變快樂吧！

## III. 短篇作文：

### Be Happy Now

There's no need to wait for happiness. You can be happy now. *First of all*, *dance* like no one is watching you. Try to *draw* something you see in your mind. *Dare to dream* of doing something great. *Moreover*, treat yourself to a good *dinner*. Have an extra serving of *dessert*. Make some *delicious food*. *Finally*, don't be afraid to *daydream*. *Watch* some funny shows on *DVD*. *Go to a* trendy *disco* and get ready to be happy now.

### 現在就變快樂

要快樂不需要等待。你現在就可以變快樂。首先,要旁若無人地跳舞。要試著畫心中看到的東西。要勇於夢想做大事。此外,要請自己吃一頓大餐。要再吃一份甜點。要做一些美食。最後,不要害怕做白日夢。要用 DVD 看一些有趣的表演。要去一間時髦的迪斯可舞廳,然後現在就準備好變快樂吧。

## IV. 填空:

D

To begin with, ___1___ to the music. ___2___ some pretty pictures. ___3___ to dream of being successful.

On the other hand, have a nice ___4___. Order the most tasty ___5___ on the menu. Indeed, you should treat yourself to ___6___ food.

Finally, spend some time ___7___. Watch some movies on ___8___. Go dancing at a ___9___ and you'll be happy.

首先,要隨著音樂起舞。要畫一些漂亮的圖畫。要勇於夢想成功。

另一方面,要好好吃一頓。要點菜單上最好吃的甜點。的確,你應該招待自己吃美食。

最後,要花一些時間做白日夢。要用 DVD 看一些電影。去迪斯可舞廳跳舞,那樣你就會很快樂。

【解答】 1. dance　2. Draw　3. Dare　4. dinner　5. dessert
6. delicious　7. daydreaming　8. DVD　9. disco

\* tasty〔'testɪ〕*adj.* 好吃的

## V. 詞彙題：

***Directions:*** *Choose the one word that best completes the sentence.*

1. _____ is fun and great exercise.
   (A) Dazzling   (B) Dancing   (C) Declining   (D) Delaying

2. You'll get a lifetime of happiness if you learn how to _____ a picture.
   (A) dodge   (B) dread   (C) drift   (D) draw

3. Great things will come when you _____ to do something impossible.
   (A) dare   (B) distort   (C) dismiss   (D) doze

4. I look forward to a nice _____ after a long day at work.
   (A) dresser   (B) dryer   (C) dinner   (D) drawer

5. No meal is complete without a serving of _____.
   (A) degree   (B) distress   (C) desert   (D) dessert

6. What's the point of eating if the food isn't _____?
   (A) delicious   (B) discreet   (C) deliberate   (D) direct

7. Many great ideas come from _____.
   (A) duckling   (B) daydreaming   (C) dwelling
   (D) diminishing

8. There are so many great films on _____ these days.
   (A) DVD   (B) MRT   (C) ATM   (D) PDA

9. Every now and then, you have to cut loose at a _____.
   (A) ditch   (B) district   (C) disco   (D) drugstore

【答案】1.(B)　2.(D)　3.(A)　4.(C)　5.(D)　6.(A)
　　　　7.(B)　8.(A)　9.(C)

## VI. 同義字整理：

1. **dance**〔 dæns 〕*v.* 跳舞
   - = rock〔 rɑk 〕
   - = swing〔 swɪŋ 〕
   - = spin〔 spɪn 〕
   - = hop〔 hɑp 〕
   - = sway〔 swe 〕
   - = whirl〔 hwɝl 〕

2. **draw**〔 drɔ 〕*v.* 畫
   - = paint〔 pent 〕
   - = sketch〔 skɛtʃ 〕
   - = depict〔 dɪ'pɪkt 〕
   - = portray〔 por'tre 〕

3. **dare**〔 dɛr 〕*v.* 敢
   - = venture〔 'vɛntʃɚ 〕
   - = have the nerve
   - = have the courage
   - = be brave enough

4. **dinner**〔 'dɪnɚ 〕*n.* 晚餐；大餐
   - = feast〔 fist 〕
   - = spread〔 sprɛd 〕
   - = evening meal
   - = main meal
   - = banquet〔 'bæŋkwɪt 〕

5. **dessert**〔 dɪ'zɝt 〕*n.* 甜點
   - = sweet〔 swit 〕
   - = afters〔 'æftɚz 〕
   - = last course
   - = sweet course

6. **delicious**〔 dɪ'lɪʃəs 〕*adj.* 美味的
   - = tasty〔 'testɪ 〕
   - = savory〔 'sevərɪ 〕
   - = yummy〔 'jʌmɪ 〕
   - = mouthwatering
     〔 'mauθ,wɔtərɪŋ 〕

7. **daydream**〔 'de,drim 〕*v.* 做白日夢
   - = dream〔 drim 〕
   - = imagine〔 ɪ'mædʒɪn 〕
   - = envision〔 ɪn'vɪʒən 〕
   - = fantasize〔 'fæntə,saɪz 〕

8. **DVD** 數位影音光碟
   - = digital video disc

9. **disco**〔 'dɪsko 〕*n.* 迪斯可舞廳
   - = discotheque〔 'dɪskə,tɛk 〕
   - = nightclub〔 'naɪt,klʌb 〕

**D**

**How to Be Happy**

# 7. E

| 看英文唸出中文 | 一口氣說九句 | 看中文唸出英文 |
|---|---|---|
| **enjoy**[2]<br>〔ɪnˈdʒɔɪ〕v. | 字首是 En | *Enjoy.*<br>要好好享受。 | 享受 |
| **engage**[3]<br>〔ɪnˈgedʒ〕v. | | *Engage.*<br>要參與。 | 從事；參與 |
| **exercise**[2]<br>〔ˈɛksəˌsaɪz〕v. n. | | *Exercise.*<br>要運動。 | 運動  |

| | | |
|---|---|---|
| **elastic**[4]<br>〔ɪˈlæstɪk〕adj. | 字尾都是 tic | Be *elastic.*<br>要有彈性。 | 有彈性的 |
| **energetic**[3]<br>〔ˌɛnəˈdʒɛtɪk〕adj. | | *Energetic.*<br>要精力充沛。 | 精力充沛的 |
| **enthusiastic**[5]<br>〔ɪnˌθjuzɪˈæstɪk〕adj. | | Very *enthusiastic.*<br>要非常熱心。 | 熱心的  |

| | | |
|---|---|---|
| **enjoyment**[2]<br>〔ɪnˈdʒɔɪmənt〕n. | 字尾都是 ment | Seek *enjoyment.*<br>要尋找樂趣。 | 樂趣 |
| **entertainment**[4]<br>〔ˌɛntəˈtenmənt〕n. | | *Entertainment.*<br>要尋找娛樂。 | 娛樂 |
| **enlightenment**[6]<br>〔ɪnˈlaɪtn̩mənt〕n. | | *Enlightenment.*<br>要尋求高人開導。 | 啟發；教導 |

E

## I. 背景說明：

*Enjoy*.（要好好享受。）( = *Get pleasure*. ) *Enjoy* your life.（要享受人生。）*Enjoy* all that life has to offer.（要享受人生的一切。）*Enjoy* yourself.（要好好玩一玩。）*Engage*.（要參與。）( = *Participate*. ) *Engage* yourself in life.（要過忙碌的生活。）( = *Be engaged in life*. )【engaged〔ɪnˋgedʒd〕*adj.* 忙的】Be an *engaged* person.（要做一個忙碌的人。）*Engage* in conversation.（要參與談話。）engage 的主要意思是「從事」，在此作「參與」解。*Exercise*. 可說成：*Exercise* daily.（要每天運動。）*Exercise* on a regular basis.（要規律運動。）【*on a regular basis* 經常；規律地 ( = *regularly* )】

*Be elastic*.（要有彈性。）( = *Be flexible*. ) 可說成：*Be* an *elastic* person.（要做一個懂得變通的人。）Have an *elastic* mind.（想法要有彈性。）*Energetic*. 在此指 Be *energetic*.（要精力充沛。）( = *Be full of energy*. ) Be an *energetic* person.（要做一個精力充沛的人。）Be *energetic* and tireless.（要精力充沛，永遠不累。）*Very enthusiastic*. 在此指 Be *very enthusiastic*.（要非常熱心。）Be an *enthusiastic* person.（要做一個熱心的人。）Be *enthusiastic* about what you're doing.（對你所做的事要熱心。）

*Seek enjoyment*. 可說成：*Seek enjoyment* and recreation.（要尋找樂趣和娛樂。）Be a person who *seeks enjoyment* and pleasure.（要做一個尋找樂趣的人。）

*Entertainment.* 在此指 Seek *entertainment.*（要尋找娛樂。）
Enjoy different types of *entertainment.*（要享受不同種類的
娛樂。）Seek regular *entertainment.*（要經常尋找娛樂。）
（ = *Seek entertainment on a regular basis.*）*Enlightenment.*
在此指 Seek *enlightenment.*（要尋求啓發。）引申為「要尋求
高人開導。」Be a person in search of *enlightenment.*（要做
一個尋求啓發的人。）enlightenment 來自於動詞 enlighten
*v.* 啓發；啓迪；開導；教導（ = *teach*；*instruct*）。Seek
*enlightenment* and wisdom.（要尋求啓發與智慧。）The
movie was *enlightening.*（那部電影有啓發性。）（ = *I learned
something from the movie.*）

*Students*, *parents*,
  *and teachers:*

Enjoy.
Engage.
Exercise.

Be elastic.
Energetic.
Very enthusiastic.

Seek enjoyment.
Entertainment.
Enlightenment.

*These are just a few of
  the keys to happiness.*

## II. 短篇英語演講：

**Students, parents, and teachers:**
各位同學、家長，和老師：

*Enjoy* your life.　要享受人生。
Be an *engaged* person.　要做一個忙碌的人。
*Exercise* on a regular basis.　要規律運動。

Have an *elastic* mind.　想法要有彈性。
Be an *energetic* person.　要做一個精力充沛的人。
Be *very enthusiastic* about what you're doing.
對你所做的事要非常熱心。

*Seek enjoyment* and recreation.　要尋找樂趣和娛樂。
Enjoy different types of *entertainment*.
要享受不同種類的娛樂。
Be a person in search of *enlightenment*.
要做一個尋求啟發的人。

**These are just a few of the keys to happiness**.
這就是一些快樂的關鍵。

## III. 短篇作文：

### The Keys to Happiness

　　Here are just a few of the keys to happiness. *For starters*,
*enjoy* all that life has to offer. *Engage* in conversation with your
friends. *And of course*, *exercise* daily. *Moreover*, *be* an *elastic*
person. Be *energetic* and tireless. Be an *enthusiastic* person.
*In a similar way*, be a person who seeks *enjoyment* and pleasure.
Get some *entertainment* on a regular basis. *And finally*, seek
*enlightenment* and wisdom, and you'll be a happy person.

### 快樂的關鍵

以下是一些快樂的關鍵。首先,要享受人生的一切。要參與和朋友的談話。當然,要每天運動。此外,要做一個懂得變通的人。要精力充沛,永遠不累。要做一個熱心的人。同樣地,要做一個尋找樂趣的人。要經常尋找娛樂。最後,要尋求啓發與智慧,那樣你就會是個快樂的人。

* key〔ki〕*n.* 關鍵　　***for starters*** 首先
wisdom〔ˋwɪzdəm〕*n.* 智慧

## IV. 填空:

Above all, ___1___ your life.  Be an ___2___ person who likes to be involved.  ___3___ on a regular basis to get your blood flowing.

Likewise, develop an ___4___ mind.  Be an ___5___ person who never gets tired.  Be ___6___ about what you're doing.

Finally, seek ___7___ and recreation.  Enjoy different types of ___8___.  Be a person in search of ___9___ and you'll find happiness.

最重要的是,要享受人生。要做一個喜歡參與,忙碌的人。要規律做運動,讓血液流動。

同樣地,要培養懂得變通的想法。要做一個充滿活力的人,永遠不會累。對你所做的事要熱心。

最後,要尋找樂趣和娛樂。要享受不同種類的娛樂。要做一個尋求啓發的人,那樣你就會找到快樂。

【解答】 1. enjoy　　2. engaged　　3. Exercise　　4. elastic
　　　　　5. energetic　　6. enthusiastic　　7. enjoyment
　　　　　8. entertainment　　9. enlightenment
　　　　　* involve〔ɪnˋvɑlv〕*v.* 使參與　　***in search of*** 尋找

## V. 詞彙題：

***Directions:*** *Choose the one word that best completes the sentence.*

1. A wise man learns to _____ the little things in life.
   (A) enjoy　(B) enact　(C) enable　(D) enforce

2. Be _____ in the moment and you'll never miss anything.
   (A) enclosed　(B) engaged　(C) enriched　(D) entitled

3. One of the pillars of good health is getting enough _____.
   (A) exercise　(B) errand　(C) essay　(D) excess

4. An _____ person bends but never breaks.
   (A) elementary　(B) exotic　(C) elastic　(D) eloquent

5. You'll get so much more done if you approach everything with an _____ attitude.
   (A) electric　(B) ethnic　(C) epidemic　(D) energetic

6. A person who is _____ about life is never without friends.
   (A) economic　(B) enthusiastic　(C) eccentric　(D) emphatic

7. Try to find _____ in the simple pleasures of life.
   (A) embarrassment　(B) element　(C) employment
   (D) enjoyment

8. If you've got some free time, why not spend it on _____?
   (A) exaggeration　(B) equality　(C) entertainment
   (D) eternity

9. It may take a while, but you can achieve _____.
   (A) enlightenment　(B) experiment　(C) equipment
   (D) environment

【答案】 1.( A )　2.( B )　3.( A )　4.( C )　5.( D )　6.( B )
　　　　 7.( D )　8.( C )　9.( A )

## VI. 同義字整理：

1. **enjoy**〔 ɪn'dʒɔɪ 〕 *v.* 享受
   - = like〔 laɪk 〕
   - = love〔 lʌv 〕
   - = delight in
   - = take pleasure in

2. **engage**〔 ɪn'gedʒ 〕 *v.* 從事；參與
   - = join in
   - = participate in
   - = take part in
   - = become involved in

3. **exercise**〔'ɛksɚ,saɪz 〕 *v. n.* 運動
   - = train〔 tren 〕
   - = drill〔 drɪl 〕
   - = work out
   - = keep fit

4. **elastic**〔 ɪ'læstɪk 〕 *adj.* 有彈性的
   - = flexible〔'flɛksəbl̩ 〕
   - = adaptable〔 ə'dæptəbl̩ 〕
   - = variable〔'vɛrɪəbl̩ 〕
   - = accommodating
     〔 ə'kɑmə,detɪŋ 〕

5. **energetic**〔,ɛnɚ'dʒɛtɪk 〕 *adj.* 精力充沛的
   - = active〔'æktɪv 〕
   - = dynamic〔 daɪ'næmɪk 〕
   - = lively〔'laɪvlɪ 〕

6. **enthusiastic**〔 ɪn,θjuzɪ'æstɪk 〕
   *adj.* 熱心的
   - = keen〔 kin 〕
   - = eager〔'igɚ 〕
   - = earnest〔'ɝnɪst 〕
   - = passionate〔'pæʃənɪt 〕

7. **enjoyment**〔 ɪn'dʒɔɪmənt 〕 *n.*
   樂趣
   - = fun〔 fʌn 〕
   - = joy〔 dʒɔɪ 〕
   - = delight〔 dɪ'laɪt 〕

   - = pleasure〔'plɛʒɚ 〕
   - = happiness〔'hæpɪnɪs 〕
   - = amusement〔 ə'mjuzmənt 〕

8. **entertainment**
   〔,ɛntɚ'tenmənt 〕 *n.* 娛樂
   - = fun〔 fʌn 〕
   - = pleasure〔'plɛʒɚ 〕
   - = leisure〔'liʒɚ 〕

   - = pastime〔'pæs,taɪm 〕
   - = recreation〔,rɛkrɪ'eʃən 〕

9. **enlightenment**
   〔 ɪn'laɪtn̩mənt 〕 *n.* 啟發；教導
   - = wisdom〔'wɪzdəm 〕
   - = knowledge〔'nɑlɪdʒ 〕
   - = understanding
     〔,ʌndɚ'stændɪŋ 〕

**How to Be Happy**

# *8.* F

| 看英文唸出中文 | 一口氣說九句 | 看中文唸出英文 |
|---|---|---|

**feast**⁴
〔 fist 〕 *v.*

**forget**¹
〔 fəˋgɛt 〕 *v.*

**forgiving**²
〔 fəˋgɪvɪŋ 〕 *adj.*

字首是 forg

*Feast*.
要大吃一頓。

*Forget*.
要忘記過去不好的事。

Be *forgiving*.
要原諒別人。

兩個動詞

大吃一頓

忘記

原諒別人的

---

**focused**²
〔ˋfokəst 〕 *adj.*

**flexible**⁴
〔ˋflɛksəb!〕 *adj.*

**friendly**²
〔ˋfrɛndlɪ 〕 *adj.*

字首是 f

**free**¹
〔 fri 〕 *adj.*

**funny**¹
〔ˋfʌnɪ 〕 *adj.*

**forward**²
〔ˋfɔrwəd 〕 *adv.*

*Focused*.
要專心。

Really *flexible*.
要很有彈性，懂得變通。

Very *friendly*.
要非常友善。

*Free*.
要自由自在。

Truly *funny*.
要很風趣。

Move *forward*.
要向前進。

專注的

有彈性的

友善的

自由的

好笑的

向前

MOVE FORWARD

F

## I. 背景説明：

  *Feast*.（要大吃一頓。）(=*Have a big meal.*) *Feast* on fresh seafood.（要吃新鮮的海鮮大餐。）*Feast* on snacks at the night market.（要在夜市狂吃小吃。）

feast 多當名詞用，作「大餐」解。Treat yourself to a *feast*.（要招待自己吃大餐。）Have a *feast* with your friends.（要和你的朋

feast

友大吃一頓。）*Forget*. 可説成：*Forget* about the past.（要忘記過去。）Forgive and *forget*.（【諺】既往不咎。）*Be forgiving*.（要原諒別人。）*Be* a *forgiving* person.（要做一個寬宏大量的人。）*Be forgiving* and kind.（要寬宏大量。）(=*Be kind and forgiving.*)

  *Focused*. 在此指 Be *focused*.（要專心。）(=*Concentrate.*) Be *focused* on your goal.（要專注於你的目標。）Be a *focused* person.（要做一個專心的人。）(=*Be a person who is focused on what he is doing.*) *Really flexible*. 在此指 Be *really flexible*.（要很有彈性。）Be a *flexible* person.（要做一個有彈性的人。）(=*Be a changeable person.*) Have a *flexible* mind.（想法要懂得變通。）(=*Have an elastic mind.*) *Very friendly*. 在此指 Be *very friendly*.（要非常友善。）(=*Be a very friendly person.*) Be *very friendly* and outgoing.（要非常友善又外向。）【outgoing〔ˈaʊtˌɡoɪŋ〕*adj.* 外向的】

***Free***. 在此指 Be ***free***. （要自由。）( = *Be without worry
or constraint.* ) Be a ***free*** thinker. （思想要自由。）( = *Be
open-minded.* ) Have a ***free*** and open attitude. （要有自由、
開放的態度。）***Truly funny***. 在此指 Be ***truly funny***. （要
非常風趣。）( = *Be a truly funny person.* ) truly 在此等於
very。Be a ***truly funny*** and free-spirited character. （要
做一個非常風趣又自由自在的人。）【free-spirited *adj.* 自由
自在的 ( = *easy-going* )】***Move forward***. （要向前進。）
( = *Advance.* ) Always be ***moving forward***. （永遠要進
步。）Be a person who is ***moving forward***. （要做一個不
斷向前進的人。）

F

***Dear friends:***

Feast.
Forget.
Be forgiving.

Focused.
Really flexible
Very friendly.

Free.
Truly funny.
Move forward.

***This is the way to happiness.***

## II. 短篇英語演講：

**Dear friends:**　親愛的朋友：

**Feast** on snacks at the night market.
要在夜市狂吃小吃。
**Forget** about the past.　要忘記過去。
**Be forgiving** and kind.　要寬宏大量。

Be **focused** on your goal.　要專注於你的目標。
Have a **really flexible** mind.　想法要非常懂得變通。
Be **very friendly** and outgoing.　要非常友善又外向。

Have a **free** and open attitude.
要有自由、開放的態度。
Be a **truly funny** person.　要做一個眞的很風趣的人。
Always be **moving forward**.　永遠要進步。

**This is the way to happiness.**　這就是快樂之道。

## III. 短篇作文：

### The Way to Happiness

Believe it or not, there is a way to happiness. *To begin with*, treat yourself to a *feast*. Forgive and *forget*. *Be a forgiving* person. *Additionally*, be a person who is *focused* on what they are doing. Have a *flexible* mind. Be a *very friendly* person. *On top of that*, be a *free* thinker. Be a *truly funny* and free-spirited character. *Above all*, be a person who is *moving forward* and you'll find the way to happiness.

### 快樂之道

信不信由你，快樂是有方法的。首先，要招待自己吃大餐。要既往不咎。要做一個寬宏大量的人。此外，要專注於自己正在做的事。想法要懂得變通。要做一個非常友善的人。此外，思想要自由。要做一個真的風趣又自由自在的人。最重要的是，要做一個不斷向前進的人，那樣你就會找到快樂之道。

* ***believe it or not*** 信不信由你　　***on top of that*** 此外
thinker〔ˋθɪŋkɚ〕*n.* 思想家；思考者
character〔ˋkærɪktɚ〕*n.* 人

## IV. 填空：

First, ___1___ on some tasty snacks at the night market. ___2___ about what happened in the past. Be ___3___ and kind.

Next, be ___4___ on your goal. Have a ___5___ mind. Be a very ___6___ and outgoing person who loves meeting new people.

More importantly, have a ___7___ and open attitude. Be a truly ___8___ person. Always be moving ___9___ and you'll find the way to happiness.

首先，要在夜市狂吃一些好吃的小吃。要忘記過去發生的事。要寬宏大量。

其次，要專注於你的目標。想法要懂得變通。要做一個非常友善又外向的人，喜歡認識新朋友。

更重要的是，要有自由、開放的態度。要做一個真的很風趣的人。永遠要進步，那樣你就會找到快樂之道。

【解答】 1. feast　2. Forget　3. forgiving　4. focused　5. flexible
　　　　 6. friendly　7. free　8. funny　9. forward

* tasty〔ˋtestɪ〕*adj.* 好吃的
snack〔snæk〕*n.* 小吃；點心　　meet〔mit〕*v.* 認識

## V. 詞彙題：

***Directions:*** *Choose the one word that best completes the sentence.*

1. It's fun to celebrate a special occasion by _____.
   (A) fetching   (B) filtering   (C) faltering   (D) feasting

2. It's better to _____ what happened in the past and look to the future.
   (A) flatter   (B) flourish   (C) forget   (D) forbid

3. A _____ person never has a heavy conscience.
   (A) following   (B) forgiving   (C) forthcoming   (D) fastening

4. Stay _____ on your goals and nothing can stop you.
   (A) frustrated   (B) frightened   (C) fascinated   (D) focused

5. Make a plan, but be _____ and willing to adjust your methods, too.
   (A) flexible   (B) facial   (C) fake   (D) false

6. A _____ person is welcome wherever he goes.
   (A) federal   (B) familiar   (C) friendly   (D) fearful

7. Everybody wants to be _____ and live according to his own rules.
   (A) feeble   (B) free   (C) financial   (D) fluent

8. A _____ comment can diffuse a tense situation.
   (A) foggy   (B) foreign   (C) formal   (D) funny

9. There's no need to look over your shoulder if you're always moving _____.
   (A) forward   (B) furthermore   (C) fairly   (D) frankly

【答案】 1.(D)   2.(C)   3.(B)   4.(D)   5.(A)   6.(C)
　　　　 7.(B)   8.(D)   9.(A)

## VI. 同義字整理：

1. **feast** 〔 fist 〕 *v.* 大吃一頓

> = consume 〔 kən'sjum 〕
> = indulge 〔 ɪn'dʌldʒ 〕
> = stuff yourself

> = eat your fill
> = eat to your heart's content

2. **forget** 〔 fɚ'gɛt 〕 *v.* 忘記

> = ignore 〔 ɪg'nor 〕
> = overlook 〔͵ovɚ'lʊk 〕
> = stop thinking about

> = dismiss from your mind
> = let bygones be bygones

3. **forgiving** 〔 fɚ'gɪvɪŋ 〕 *adj.* 原諒
別人的；寬容的

> = lenient 〔 'linɪənt 〕
> = tolerant 〔 'tɑlərənt 〕
> = compassionate 〔 kəm'pæʃənɪt 〕

> = gracious 〔 'greʃəs 〕
> = merciful 〔 'mɝsɪfəl 〕

4. **focused** 〔 'fokəst 〕 *adj.* 專注的

> = single-minded
> 〔 'sɪŋgl̩'maɪndɪd 〕
> = determined 〔 dɪ'tɝmɪnd 〕
> = resolute 〔 'rɛzə͵lut 〕

5. **flexible** 〔 'flɛksəbl̩ 〕 *adj.* 有彈
性的；懂得變通的

> = elastic 〔 ɪ'læstɪk 〕
> = variable 〔 'vɛrɪəbl̩ 〕
> = adaptable 〔 ə'dæptəbl̩ 〕
> = accommodating
> 〔 ə'kɑmə͵detɪŋ 〕

6. **friendly** 〔 'frɛndlɪ 〕 *adj.* 友善的

> = kind 〔 kaɪnd 〕
> = warm 〔 wɔrm 〕
> = welcoming 〔 'wɛlkəmɪŋ 〕
> = amiable 〔 'emɪəbl̩ 〕

7. **free** 〔 fri 〕 *adj.* 自由的

> = easy 〔 'izɪ 〕
> = easy-going 〔 'izɪ͵goɪŋ 〕
> = loose 〔 lus 〕

> = liberal 〔 'lɪbərəl 〕
> = relaxed 〔 rɪ'lækst 〕

8. **funny** 〔 'fʌnɪ 〕 *adj.* 好笑的

> = silly 〔 'sɪlɪ 〕
> = comic 〔 'kɑmɪk 〕
> = humorous 〔 'hjumərəs 〕

> = amusing 〔 ə'mjuzɪŋ 〕
> = entertaining 〔͵ɛntɚ'tenɪŋ 〕

9. **forward** 〔 'fɔrwɚd 〕 *adv.* 向前

> = ahead 〔 ə'hɛd 〕
> = forth 〔 forθ 〕
> = onwards 〔 'ɑnwɚdz 〕
> = towards the front

**F**

**How to Be Happy**

# 9. G

| 看英文唸出中文 | 一口氣說九句 | 看中文唸出英文 |
|---|---|---|
| **golf**[2] <br> 〔 gɑlf , gɔlf 〕 *n.* | 兩種運動 { Go **golfing**. <br> 要打高爾夫球。 | 打高爾夫球 |
| **gym**[3] <br> 〔 dʒɪm 〕 *n.* | To the **gym**. <br> 要上健身房。 | 健身房  |
| **gallery**[4] <br> 〔 'gælərɪ 〕 *n.* | A **gallery**. <br> 要去畫廊。 | 畫廊 |
| **goal**[2] <br> 〔 gol 〕 *n.* | 三個名詞 { Have a **goal**. <br> 要有目標。 | 目標 |
| **gathering**[5] <br> 〔 'gæðərɪŋ 〕 *n.* | Have a **gathering**. <br> 要有聚會。 | 聚會  |
| **guitar**[2] <br> 〔 gɪ'tɑr 〕 *n.* | Play the **guitar**. <br> 要彈吉他。 | 吉他 |
| **grateful**[4] <br> 〔 'gretfəl 〕 *adj.* | 兩個形容詞 { Be **grateful**. <br> 要心存感激。 | 感激的 |
| **generous**[2] <br> 〔 'dʒɛnərəs 〕 *adj.* | Very **generous**. <br> 要非常慷慨。 | 慷慨的 |
| **globe-trotter** <br> 〔 'glob,trɑtɚ 〕 *n.* | A **globe-trotter**. <br> 要去環遊世界。 | 環遊世界的人  |

## I. 背景說明：

*Go golfing*. 可説成：Let's *go golfing*, shall we?（我們去打高爾夫球，好嗎？）shall we 是 shall we go 的省略。Do you want to *go golfing*?（你想不想去打高爾夫球？）*To the gym*. 在此指 Go *to the gym*.（要上健身房。）Go *to the gym* twice a week.（一個禮拜要去兩次健身房。）Go *to the gym* every day.（要每天上健身房。）*A gallery*. 在此指 Go to *a gallery*.（要去畫廊。）可説成：Visit *a gallery*.（要去畫廊。）Take a trip to *a gallery*.（要去畫廊看看。）gallery 的意思有：①美術館；展覽館②畫廊③陳列室。

gym

gallery

G

*Have a goal*.（要有目標。）( = *Have a target.*) *Have a goal* in mind.（心中要有目標。）Set a *goal* for yourself.（要為你自己設定一個目標。）*Have a gathering*. ( = *Have a party.*) Host *a gathering* at your home.（要在你的家裡舉辦聚會。）【host〔host〕v. 主辦】Attend *a gathering* in the neighborhood.（要參加鄰居舉辦的聚會。）( = *Go to a party held by your neighbor.*) 在美國，鄰居往往會舉行聚會（gathering），邀請左右鄰居參加。*Play the guitar*. 句中「pay＋the＋樂器名稱」一定要有定冠詞 the。Learn to *play the guitar*.（要學會彈吉他。）Learn to *play the guitar* well.（要學習把吉他彈好。）

　　*Be grateful.* ( = *Be thankful.* ) **Be** a **grateful** person. ( 要
做一個心存感激的人。) **Be grateful** for everything you have.
( 要對你所擁有的一切心存感激。) Have a **grateful** attitude.
( 要有心存感激的態度。) *Very generous.* 在此指 Be **very
generous**. ( 要非常慷慨。) ( = *Be a very generous person.* )
Have a **very generous** spirit. ( 要有非常慷慨的精神。) *A
globe-trotter.* 在此指 Be **a globe-trotter**. ( 要去環遊世界。)
Be **a** tireless **globe-trotter**. ( 要做一個永不厭倦的環遊世界的
人。) ( = *Be a persistent globe-trotter.* ) globe-trotter 字面的
意思是「像馬一樣慢跑，環遊世界」，引申為「環遊世界的人」
( = *world-traveler* )。

**G**

*Ladies and gentlemen,
  your attention, please:*

Go golfing.
To the gym.
A gallery.

Have a goal.
Have a gathering.
Play the guitar.

Be grateful.
Very generous.
A globe-trotter.

*These are the steps
  to happiness.*

## II. 短篇英語演講：

***Ladies and gentlemen**, **your attention**, **please:***
各位先生、各位女士，請注意：

Let's ***go golfing**, shall we?　我們去打高爾夫球，好嗎？
Go ***to the gym** twice a week.　一個禮拜要去兩次健身房。
Take a trip to ***a gallery**.　要去畫廊看看。

***Have a goal** in mind.　心中要有目標。
Host ***a gathering** at your home.　要在你的家裡舉辦聚會。
Learn to ***play the guitar**.　要學會彈吉他。

***Be grateful** for everything you have.*
要對你所擁有的一切心存感激。
Have a ***very generous** spirit.　要有非常慷慨的精神。
Be *a* tireless ***globe-trotter**.　要做一個永不厭倦的環遊世界的人。

***These are the steps to happiness**.　這些就是要快樂的步驟。

## III. 短篇作文：

### The Steps to Happiness

If the secret of happiness is to stay in motion, here are a few steps to keep you moving. *First*, ***go golfing** with your friends.  Go ***to the gym** every day and work up a sweat.  After that, visit ***an** art ***gallery** to stimulate your brain.  *Moreover*, ***have a goal** in mind.  Attend ***a gathering** in the neighborhood.  Maybe learn to ***play the guitar**.  *On top of that*, be a ***grateful** and ***generous** person.  The final step is to be ***a globe-trotter**.  Get out there and see the world.  *For sure*, happiness is guaranteed.

### 要快樂的步驟

　　如果快樂的祕訣是動個不停，那這裡有一些能使你動個不停的步驟。首先，要和你的朋友去打高爾夫球。要每天上健身房，練出一身汗。之後，要去美術館看看，刺激你的頭腦。而且，心中要有目標。要參加鄰居舉辦的聚會。也許要學會彈吉他。此外，要做一個心存感激而且慷慨的人。最後一步，就是要去環遊世界。要出去看看世界。當然，這樣就一定會快樂。

　　\* motion〔'moʃən〕*n.* 移動　　**in motion** 在移動中
　　**work up** 通過激烈活動出（一身汗）　　sweat〔swɛt〕*n.* 流汗
　　**art gallery** 美術館；畫廊　　stimulate〔'stɪmjə,let〕*v.* 刺激
　　**for sure** 當然　　guarantee〔,gærən'ti〕*v.* 保證

## IV. 填空：

　　I've got an idea: Let's go ___1___, shall we?  Let's go to the ___2___ twice a week.  And then, let's take a trip to a ___3___.

　　Meanwhile, set a ___4___ for yourself.  Host a ___5___ at your home.  Learn to play a musical instrument, like the ___6___.

　　Of course, be ___7___ for everything you have.  What's more, have a very ___8___ spirit.  Be a tireless ___9___ and happiness will come.

　　我有一個想法：我們去打高爾夫球，好嗎？我們一個禮拜去兩次健身房吧。然後，我們再去畫廊看看。

　　同時，要為你自己設定一個目標。要在你的家裡舉辦聚會。要學習彈奏樂器，像是吉他。

　　當然，要對你所擁有的一切心存感激。此外，要有非常慷慨的精神。要做一個永不厭倦的環遊世界的人，然後快樂就會來臨。

【解答】 1. golfing　2. gym　3. gallery　4. goal　5. gathering
　　　　　6. guitar　7. grateful　8. generous　9. globe-trotter
　　　　　\* **I've got** 我有（= I have）　　instrument〔'ɪnstrəmənt〕*n.* 樂器
　　　　　**musical instrument** 樂器　　tireless〔'taɪrlɪs〕*adj.* 不會疲倦的

## V. 詞彙題：

*Directions: Choose the one word that best completes the sentence.*

1. A lot of big business deals are closed during a round of _____.
   (A) gospel　(B) golf　(C) goose　(D) gold

2. Hit the _____ for a vigorous workout.
   (A) gym　(B) grocery　(C) grave　(D) ground

3. Spend some time browsing an art _____.
   (A) gallon　(B) garbage　(C) galaxy　(D) gallery

4. Set a _____ for yourself and let nothing stop you from reaching it.
   (A) goat　(B) gown　(C) goal　(D) gorge

5. Enjoy yourself at a _____ of your closest friends.
   (A) graph　(B) gathering　(C) gravity　(D) gulf

6. It takes practice, but you'll eventually get good at playing the _____.
   (A) guava　(B) garlic　(C) ginger　(D) guitar

7. It's important to show others that you are _____ for their help.
   (A) general　(B) glorious　(C) grateful　(D) graphic

8. Being _____ isn't limited to money.
   (A) generous　(B) gifted　(C) gloomy　(D) gradual

9. We all envy the _____ who's been everywhere.
   (A) grammar　(B) glacier　(C) globe-trotter　(D) grasshopper

【答案】 1.(B)　2.(A)　3.(D)　4.(C)　5.(B)　6.(D)
　　　　 7.(C)　8.(A)　9.(C)

## VI. 同義字整理：

1. **golf** 〔 gɑlf , gɔlf 〕 *n.* 高爾夫球
   *v.* 打高爾夫球
   - = a game played on a large open course, the object of which is to hit a ball using clubs, with as few strokes as possible, into each of usually 18 holes

2. **gym** 〔 dʒɪm 〕 *n.* 健身房
   - = gymnasium 〔 dʒɪm'nezɪəm 〕
   - = a building or part of a building with facilities for exercise, bodybuilding, or other kinds of physical training

3. **gallery** 〔'gælərɪ 〕 *n.* 畫廊；
   美術館；陳列室
   - = exhibition room
   - = display room
   - = museum 〔 mju'zɪəm 〕

4. **goal** 〔 gol 〕 *n.* 目標
   - = aim 〔 em 〕
   - = end 〔 ɛnd 〕
   - = target 〔'tɑrgɪt 〕

- = purpose 〔'pɝpəs 〕
- = objective 〔 əb'dʒɛktɪv 〕
- = ambition 〔 æm'bɪʃən 〕

5. **gathering** 〔'gæðərɪŋ 〕 *n.* 聚會
   - = assembly 〔 ə'sɛmblɪ 〕
   - = get-together 〔'gɛt tə,gɛðɚ 〕
   - = party 〔'pɑrtɪ 〕

6. **guitar** 〔 gɪ'tɑr 〕 *n.* 吉他
   - = a stringed instrument usually having six strings; played by strumming or plucking

7. **grateful** 〔'gretfəl 〕 *adj.* 感激的
   - = thankful 〔'θæŋkfəl 〕
   - = obliged 〔 ə'blaɪdʒd 〕
   - = indebted 〔 ɪn'dɛtɪd 〕
   - = appreciative 〔 ə'priʃɪ,etɪv 〕

8. **generous** 〔'dʒɛnərəs 〕 *adj.* 慷慨的
   - = liberal 〔'lɪbərəl 〕
   - = charitable 〔'tʃærətəbl 〕
   - = hospitable 〔'hɑspɪtəbl 〕
   - = unselfish 〔 ʌn'sɛlfɪʃ 〕

9. **globe-trotter** 〔'glob,trɑtɚ 〕 *n.*
   環遊世界的人
   - = globe-trekker 〔'glob,trɛkɚ 〕
   - = world traveler

**How to Be Happy**

# *10.* H

| 看英文唸出中文 | 一口氣說九句 | 看中文唸出英文 |
|---|---|---|
| **hope**[1]<br>〔 hop 〕 *n.* | Have *hope*.<br>要有希望。 | 希望 |
| **health**[1]<br>〔 hɛlθ 〕 *n.* | *Health*.<br>要健康。 | 健康 |
| **harmony**[4]<br>〔'hɑrmənɪ 〕 *n.* | *Harmony*.<br>要和諧。 | 和諧 |
| **humor**[2]<br>〔'hjumɚ 〕 *n.* | *Humor*.<br>要有幽默感。 | 幽默 |
| **hobby**[2]<br>〔'hɑbɪ 〕 *n.* | A *hobby*.<br>要有嗜好。 | 嗜好 |
| **hairdo**[5]<br>〔'hɛr͵du 〕 *n.* | Get a new *hairdo*.<br>要剪個新髮型。 | 髮型 |
| **hug**[3]<br>〔 hʌg 〕 *v. n.* | *Hug* somebody.<br>要擁抱某人。 | 擁抱 |
| **heart**[1]<br>〔 hart 〕 *n.* | Follow your *heart*.<br>要聽從你的心意。 | 心 |
| **holiday**[1]<br>〔'hɑlə͵de 〕 *n.* | Go on a *holiday*.<br>要去度假。 | 假日；<br>假期 |

四個名詞

句意相關

H

# I. 背景說明：

　　*Have hope*. ( = *Be optimistic or faithful.* ) Be a person with *hope*. ( 要做一個懷有希望的人。) *Have* positive *hopes* for the future. ( 要對未來抱有樂觀的希望。) *Health*. 在此指 Have *health*. ( 要健康。) Take care of your *health*. ( 要照顧你的健康。) Mind your *health*. ( 要注意你的健康。) *Harmony*. 在此指 Have *harmony*. ( 要和諧。) ( = *Be a peaceful person.* = *Get along with people.* ) Have *harmony* with people around you. ( 和你周圍的人要和諧。) Seek *harmony*. ( 要尋求和諧。) Promote *harmony*. ( 要促進和諧。) harmony 的意思有：①和諧②和睦；融洽③平靜。

　　*Humor*. 在此指 Have *humor*. ( 要有幽默感。) ( = *Have a sense of humor.* ) Be a person with a good sense of *humor*. ( 要做一個很有幽默感的人。) *A hobby*. 在此指 Have *a hobby*. ( 要有嗜好。) Have *an* interesting *hobby*. ( 要有有趣的嗜好。) Have more than one *hobby*. ( 要有不只一個嗜好。) *Get a new hairdo*. 可說成：Treat yourself to *a new hairdo*. ( 要送給自己一個新髮型。) Try *a new hairdo*. ( 要嘗試新的髮型。) 不可說成：*Have a new hairdo*. ( 誤 )

　　*Hug somebody*. ( 要擁抱某人。) ( = *Embrace somebody.* ) 美國的文化是，當眾擁抱是被允許的，私下擁抱是騷擾。要擁抱異性前，可先跟對方說：Give me a *hug*. ( 抱我一下。) 如果她拒絕，通常會說：I'd rather not. ( 我寧願不要。) 如

果同意，就會說：Sure.（當然。）*Hug* someone you love.
（要擁抱你愛的人。）*Hug* a friend.（要擁抱一個朋友。）
*Hug somebody* today.（今天要擁抱一個人。）擁抱會使你
快樂，有助於健康。*Follow your heart.*（= *Follow your
feelings.*）有一句名言：When you're in doubt, *follow
your heart*, not your mind.（當你心存懷疑時，要跟著你的心
意走，而不是你的理智。）*Follow your heart* wherever it
goes.（要隨心所欲。）Listen to your *heart*.（要傾聽你內心
的聲音。）*Follow your heart*, and you'll be happy.（隨心所
欲會很快樂。）Follow your mind, and you'll do logical
things.（跟著你的理智走，你會做合理的事。）*Go on a
holiday.*（= *Go on a vacation.*）*Go on a* summer *holiday*.
（要去過暑假。）（= *Go on a summer vacation.*）Treat yourself
to a *holiday*.（要招待自己去度假。）*Go on a holiday.* 中的
on 表示目的，含有「從事」的意思，後面常接 business,
errand, journey, trip 之類的字。【詳見「文法寶典」p.595】

$$
\text{go on a(n)}
\begin{cases}
\text{trip　去旅行} \\
\text{journey　去旅行} \\
\text{tour　去旅行} \\
\text{hike　去健行} \\
\text{picnic　去野餐} \\
\text{excursion　去遠足} \\
\text{outing　去郊遊}
\end{cases}
$$

H

## II. 英語演講：

### 【一字英語演講】

*Dear ladies and*
  *gentlemen:*

*Have hope.*
*Health.*
*Harmony.*

*Humor.*
*A hobby.*
*Get a new hairdo.*

*Hug somebody.*
*Follow your heart.*
*Go on a holiday.*

*Do this*, *and*
  *happiness will*
  *be yours.*

### 【短篇英語演講】

*Dear ladies and gentlemen:*
親愛的各位先生、各位女士：

*Have* positive *hopes* for the future.
要對未來抱有樂觀的希望。
Take care of your *health*.  要照顧你的健康。
Promote *harmony*.  要促進和諧。

Be a person with a good sense of *humor*.
要做一個很有幽默感的人。
Have *an* interesting *hobby*.  要有有趣的嗜好。
Try *getting a new hairdo*.  要嘗試剪個新髮型。

*Hug somebody* today.  今天要擁抱一個人。
*Follow your heart* wherever it goes.  要隨心所欲。
Plan to *go on a holiday*.  要計劃去度假。

*Do this*, *and happiness will be yours*.
如果能這麼做，快樂就會是你的。

## III. 短篇作文：

### Happiness Can Be Yours

　　Great news!  Happiness can be yours, if you follow these steps.  *First*, *have* positive *hopes* for the future.  Mind your *health*.  Have *harmony* with people around you.  *On top of that*, have a sense of *humor*.  Have more than one *hobby*.  *Moreover*, *get a new hairdo*.  *Meanwhile*, *hug somebody* today.  When you're in doubt, *follow your heart*, not your mind.  *Go on a* summer *holiday* and happiness will be yours.

H

### 快樂可以是你的

好消息！如果你遵照這些步驟，快樂就可以是你的。首先，要對未來抱有樂觀的希望。要注意你的健康。和你周圍的人要和諧。而且，要有幽默感。要有不只一個嗜好。此外，要剪個新髮型。同時，今天要擁抱一個人。當你心存懷疑時，要跟你的心意走，而不是你的理智。要去過暑假，這樣快樂就會是你的。

\* news〔njuz〕*n.* 消息　　follow〔'falo〕*v.* 遵循；聽從
positive〔'pazətɪv〕*adj.* 樂觀的　　mind〔maɪnd〕*v.* 注意
**in doubt** 懷疑的

## IV. 填空：

In order to be happy, be a person with ____1____. Take care of your ____2____ by eating right and getting lots of exercise. And then, promote ____3____.

Meanwhile, be a person with a good sense of ____4____. Pick up an interesting ____5____. Treat yourself to a new ____6____.

Additionally, ____7____ someone you love. Follow your ____8____, and you'll be happy. Treat yourself to a ____9____ and happiness will be yours.

要快樂，就要做一個懷有希望的人。要照顧你的健康，吃對的食物，做很多的運動。然後，要促進和諧。

同時，要做一個很有幽默感的人。要學會一個有趣的嗜好。要送給自己一個新髮型。

此外，要擁抱你愛的人。隨心所欲會很快樂。要招待自己去度假，那你就會很快樂。

【解答】 1. hope　　2. health　　3. harmony　　4. humor　　5. hobby
6. hairdo　　7. hug　　8. heart　　9. holiday

\* promote〔prə'mot〕*v.* 促進　　**pick up** 學會
trcat〔trit〕*v.* 招待　　additionally〔ə'dɪʃənlɪ〕*adv.* 此外

## V. 詞彙題：

***Directions:*** *Choose the one word that best completes the sentence.*

1. Never give up _____ and keep fighting until the very end.
   (A) hole   (B) hope   (C) hint   (D) hive

2. Without _____, a man has nothing.
   (A) horn   (B) hatred   (C) headline   (D) health

3. Everything is so much better when there is _____ in the community.
   (A) hostility   (B) humidity   (C) harmony   (D) hypocrisy

4. A good sense of _____ is key to happiness.
   (A) humor   (B) hanger   (C) hunger   (D) horror

5. A _____ will keep you busy and interested in something constructive.
   (A) hockey   (B) habitat   (C) habit   (D) hobby

6. Nothing can change your outlook on life like a new _____.
   (A) hazard   (B) hippo   (C) hairdo   (D) headline

7. If someone is looking down, give them a _____.
   (A) hunch   (B) hug   (C) hedge   (D) hostage

8. Follow your _____ wherever it goes.
   (A) host   (B) helmet   (C) hardship   (D) heart

9. There is no happier feeling than being on a _____.
   (A) holiday   (B) hallway   (C) harvest   (D) honey

【答案】 1.(B)   2.(D)   3.(C)   4.(A)   5.(D)   6.(C)
　　　　 7.(B)   8.(D)   9.(A)

## VI. 同義字整理：

1. **hope** 〔 hop 〕 *n.* 希望
   - = faith 〔 feθ 〕
   - = belief 〔 bɪ'lif 〕
   - = expectation 〔 ͵ɛkspɛk'teʃən 〕

   - = confidence 〔 'kɑnfədəns 〕
   - = dream 〔 drim 〕

2. **health** 〔 hɛlθ 〕 *n.* 健康
   - = fitness 〔 'fɪtnɪs 〕
   - = wellness 〔 'wɛlnɪs 〕
   - = good condition

3. **harmony** 〔 'hɑrmənɪ 〕 *n.* 和諧
   - = unity 〔 'junətɪ 〕
   - = accord 〔 ə'kɔrd 〕
   - = order 〔 'ɔrdɚ 〕

   - = peace 〔 pis 〕
   - = agreement 〔 ə'grimənt 〕

4. **humor** 〔 'hjumɚ 〕 *n.* 幽默
   - = funniness 〔 'fʌnɪnɪs 〕
   - = the quality that makes something laughable or amusing
   - = the ability to perceive, enjoy, or express what is amusing, comical, incongruous or absurd

5. **hobby** 〔 'hɑbɪ 〕 *n.* 嗜好
   - = pastime 〔 'pæs͵taɪm 〕
   - = leisure pursuit
   - = leisure activity

6. **hairdo** 〔 'hɛr͵du 〕 *n.* 髮型
   - = hairstyle 〔 'hɛr͵staɪl 〕
   - = the arrangement of the hair

7. **hug** 〔 hʌg 〕 *v. n.* 擁抱
   - = embrace 〔 ɪm'bres 〕
   - = hold 〔 hold 〕
   - = cuddle 〔 'kʌdl̩ 〕
   - = clasp 〔 klæsp 〕

8. **heart** 〔 hɑrt 〕 *n.* 心；感情
   - = soul 〔 sol 〕
   - = feelings 〔 'filɪŋz 〕
   - = emotions 〔 ɪ'moʃənz 〕
   - = sentiments 〔 'sɛntəmənts 〕

9. **holiday** 〔 'hɑlə͵de 〕 *n.* 假日；假期
   - = vacation 〔 ve'keʃən 〕
   - = leave 〔 liv 〕
   - = break 〔 brek 〕
   - = time off

**H**

**How to Be Happy**

# *11.* I

| 看英文唸出中文 | 一 口 氣 説 九 句 | 看中文唸出英文 |
|---|---|---|
| **inspire**[4]<br>〔 ɪn'spaɪr 〕v. | 字首都是 in { | Be *inspired*.<br>要充滿熱忱。 | 激勵 |
| **indifferent**[5]<br>〔 ɪn'dɪfrənt 〕adj. | | *Indifferent*.<br>要不在乎。 | 字尾是 ent | 漠不關心的;<br>不在乎的 |
| **independent**[2]<br>〔ˌɪndɪ'pɛndənt 〕adj. | | *Independent*.<br>要獨立自主。 | 獨立的 |

| **intimacy**[6]<br>〔'ɪntəməsɪ 〕n. | 字首是 int { | Seek *intimacy*.<br>要尋找知己。 | 親密 |
| **interaction**[4]<br>〔ˌɪntə'ækʃən 〕n. | | *Interaction*.<br>要尋求互動。 | 字尾是 tion | 互動 |
| **invention**[4]<br>〔 ɪn'vɛnʃən 〕n. | | *Invention*.<br>要尋求發明。 | 發明<br> |

| **imagine**[2]<br>〔 ɪ'mædʒɪn 〕v. | 字首是 In { | *Imagine*.<br>要會想像。 | 想像 |
| **invite**[2]<br>〔 ɪn'vaɪt 〕v. | | *Invite* others.<br>要邀請別人。 | 邀請 |
| **Internet**[4]<br>〔'ɪntə͵nɛt 〕n. | | Surf the *Internet*.<br>要上網。 | 網際網路 |

## I. 背景說明：

*Be inspired*. 字面的意思是「要受到激勵。」在這裡的意思是「要熱心；要充滿熱忱。」( = *Be enthusiastic*. ) 對於別人講的話，要有熱情的反應，才會使你快樂。*Be* an *inspired* person. ( 要做一個充滿熱忱的人。) *Be inspired* by the world around you. ( 要受到周圍世界的激勵。)( = *Be inspired by your environment*. ) inspire 的主要意思是「激勵」，如 Are you *inspired*? ( 你受到激勵了沒有？) I'm *inspired*. ( 我受到了激勵。)【詳見「一口氣背會話」p.711】*Indifferent*. 在此指 Be *indifferent*. ( 要不在乎。) Be *indifferent* to negative people. ( 不要在乎悲觀的人。) Have an *indifferent* attitude. ( 要有不在乎的態度。) indifferent 的意思有：①漠不關心的 ( = *unconcerned* ) ②不在乎的 ( = *careless* )。*Independent*. 在此指 Be *independent*. ( 要獨立。)( = *Be an independent person*. ) Have an *independent* spirit. ( 要有獨立的精神。)

*Seek intimacy*. ( = *Seek close relationships*. ) *Seek* lasting *intimacy* with another person. ( 要尋求和另一個人持久的親密關係。) Establish *intimacy* with your partner. ( 要和你的夥伴建立親密關係。) *Interaction*. 在此指 Seek *interaction*. ( 要尋求互動。) Seek *interaction* with others. ( 要尋求和別人的互動。) Promote *interaction* with your peers. ( 要促進和同儕之間的互動。)【peer〔pɪr〕*n.* 同儕；同輩】*Invention*. 在此指 Seek *invention*. ( 要尋求發明。) Seek *invention* and creativity. ( 要尋求發明和創造力。) Seek *invention* to improve your life. ( 要尋求發明，改善你的生活。) 所謂 invention ( 發明 )，包含一切，如生活方式、做事情的方式等。

*Imagine.* ( = *Think* ) 可説成：***Imagine*** your ideal future. ( 要想像你理想的未來。) ***Imagine*** the possibilities. ( 要想像可能性。) ***Invite others.*** 可説成：***Invite others*** to dinner. ( 要邀請別人吃晚餐。) ***Invite*** people to have a drink. ( 要邀請大家喝一杯酒。) 在美國，原則上，邀請的人會付錢請客。***Surf the Internet.*** ( = *Browse the Internet.* = *Browse the Web.* ) ***Surf the Internet*** for information. ( 要上網找資料。) ***Surf the Internet*** for interesting articles. ( 要上網找有趣的文章。)【surf〔sɝf〕*v.* 衝浪；上 ( 網 )】

*My dearest students:*

Be inspired.
Indifferent.
Independent.

Seek intimacy.
Interaction.
Invention.

Imagine.
Invite others.
Surf the Internet.

*These are nine keys to happiness.*

## II. 短篇英語演講：

> *My dearest students:* 我最親愛的同學們：
>
> *Be* an *inspired* person. 要做一個充滿熱忱的人。
> Be *indifferent* to negative people. 不要在乎悲觀的人。
> Have an *independent* spirit. 要有獨立的精神。
>
> *Seek* lasting *intimacy* with another person.
> 要尋求和另一個人持久的親密關係。
> Seek *interaction* with others. 要尋求和別人的互動。
> Seek *invention* and creativity. 要尋求發明和創造力。
>
> *Imagine* the possibilities. 要想像可能性。
> *Invite others* to dinner. 要邀請別人吃晚餐。
> *Surf the Internet* for information. 要上網找資料。
>
> *These are nine keys to happiness.*
> 這些就是快樂的九個關鍵。

## III. 短篇作文：

### Nine Keys to Happiness

Here are nine keys to happiness. One: *Be inspired* by the world around you. Two: Have an *indifferent* attitude. Three: Be an *independent* person. Four: Establish *intimacy* with your partner. Five: Promote *interaction* with your peers. Six: Seek *invention* to improve your life. Seven: *Imagine* your ideal future. Eight: *Invite* people to have a drink. *And last but not least*: *Surf the Internet* for interesting articles.

### 快樂的九個關鍵

以下是快樂的九個關鍵。一、要受到周圍世界的激勵。二、要有不在乎的態度。三、要做一個獨立的人。四、要和你的夥伴建立親密關係。五、要促進和同儕之間的互動。六、要尋求發明,改善你的生活。七、要想像你理想的未來。八、要邀請大家喝一杯。最後一項要點是:要上網找有趣的文章。

* key〔ki〕*n.* 關鍵　　attitude〔'ætə,tjud〕*n.* 態度
establish〔ə'stæblɪʃ〕*v.* 建立　　promote〔prə'mot〕*v.* 促進
***last but not least*** 最後一項要點是

## IV. 填空:

First of all, be an ___1___ person, full of energy and vigor.
Be ___2___ to negative people.  Have an ___3___ spirit.

Additionally, seek lasting ___4___ with another person.  Seek
___5___ with others.  Seek ___6___ and creativity to improve
your life.

Moreover, ___7___ the possibilities.  ___8___ others to
dinner.  And finally, surf the ___9___ for information.

首先,要做一個很有熱忱的人,要充滿活力。不要在乎悲觀的人。要有獨立的精神。

此外,要尋求和另一個人持久的親密關係。要尋求和別人的互動。要尋求發明和創造力,改善你的生活。

此外,要想像可能性。要邀請別人吃晚餐。最後,要上網找資料。

【解答】 1. inspired　2. indifferent　3. independent
4. intimacy　5. interaction　6. invention　7. imagine
8. Invite　9. Internet

* energy〔'ɛnədʒɪ〕*n.* 精力;活力　　vigor〔'vɪgə〕*n.* 精力;活力
lasting〔'læstɪŋ〕*adj.* 持久的
creativity〔,krie'tɪvətɪ〕*n.* 創造力

## V. 詞彙題：

***Directions:*** *Choose the one word that best completes the sentence.*

1. Look for ways to be _____ and you'll surely be happy.
   (A) intruded　(B) injured　(C) insulted　(D) inspired

2. Be _____ to all the chaos that surrounds you.
   (A) inherent　(B) indifferent　(C) ideal　(D) identical

3. Learn how to be an _____ and free thinker.
   (A) imperial　(B) indignant　(C) independent
   (D) ignorant

4. Seek to create _____ with your partner.
   (A) intimacy　(B) identity　(C) inquiry　(D) irony

5. A lot can be accomplished if you seek _____ with others.
   (A) inflation　(B) intention　(C) impression　(D) interaction

6. They say that the mother of _____ is necessity.
   (A) interruption　(B) injection　(C) invention　(D) instruction

7. It doesn't cost you anything to _____ a better future.
   (A) imitate　(B) imagine　(C) imply　(D) impose

8. If you're bored, _____ a friend to take a walk in the park.
   (A) invite　(B) inherit　(C) interfere　(D) indulge

9. The _____ is full of useful information.
   (A) Impulse　(B) Instinct　(C) Interval　(D) Internet

【答案】1. ( D )　2. ( B )　3. ( C )　4. ( A )　5. ( D )　6. ( C )
　　　　7. ( B )　8. ( A )　9. ( D )

# VI. 同義字整理：

1. **inspire**〔ɪnˈspaɪr〕*v.* 激勵
   = stimulate〔ˈstɪmjə͵let〕
   = arouse〔əˈraʊz〕
   = uplift〔ʌpˈlɪft〕
   = stir up

2. **indifferent**〔ɪnˈdɪfrənt〕*adj.*
   漠不關心的；不在乎的
   = unconcerned〔͵ʌnkənˈsɜnd〕
   = detached〔dɪˈtætʃt〕
   = distant〔ˈdɪstənt〕
   = cool〔kul〕

3. **independent**〔͵ɪndɪˈpɛndənt〕
   *adj.* 獨立的
   = neutral〔ˈnjutrəl〕
   = objective〔əbˈdʒɛktɪv〕
   = free〔fri〕

   = fair〔fɛr〕
   = open-minded
     〔ˈopənˈmaɪndɪd〕

4. **intimacy**〔ˈɪntəməsɪ〕*n.* 親密
   = familiarity〔fə͵mɪlɪˈærətɪ〕
   = closeness〔ˈklosnɪs〕
   = confidence〔ˈkɑnfədəns〕
   = caring〔ˈkɛrɪŋ〕

5. **interaction**〔͵ɪntɚˈækʃən〕*n.*
   互動
   = contact〔ˈkɑntækt〕
   = interplay〔ˈɪntɚ͵ple〕
   = interchange〔͵ɪntɚˈtʃendʒ〕

6. **invention**〔ɪnˈvɛnʃən〕*n.* 發明
   = creativity〔͵krieˈtɪvətɪ〕
   = originality〔ə͵rɪdʒəˈnælətɪ〕
   = ingenuity〔͵ɪndʒəˈnjuətɪ〕

7. **imagine**〔ɪˈmædʒɪn〕*v.* 想像
   = see〔si〕
   = picture〔ˈpɪktʃɚ〕
   = envision〔ɪnˈvɪʒən〕

   = visualize〔ˈvɪʒʊəl͵aɪz〕
   = dream up

8. **invite**〔ɪnˈvaɪt〕*v.* 邀請
   = ask〔æsk〕
   = seek〔sik〕
   = call for

   = ask for
   = request the pleasure of
     *one's* company

9. **Internet**〔ˈɪntɚ͵nɛt〕*n.* 網際網路
   = Net〔nɛt〕
   = Web〔wɛb〕
   = World Wide Web

# How to Be Happy

# *12.* L

| 看英文唸出中文 | 一口氣說九句 | 看中文唸出英文 |
|---|---|---|
| **laugh**[1] <br> 〔 læf 〕 v. | *Laugh*. <br> 要笑。 | 笑 |
| **loose**[3] <br> 〔 lus 〕 adj. | Stay *loose*. <br> 要放鬆。 | 鬆的 |
| **love**[1] <br> 〔 lʌv 〕 n. v. | Fall in *love*. <br> 要談戀愛。 | 愛 |
| **lovely**[2] <br> 〔 ˈlʌvlɪ 〕 adj. | Be *lovely*. <br> 要可愛。 | 可愛的 |
| **lovable** <br> 〔 ˈlʌvəbḷ 〕 adj. | *Lovable*. <br> 要討人喜歡。 | 可愛的；討人喜歡的 |
| **logical**[4] <br> 〔 ˈlɑdʒɪkḷ 〕 adj. | Very *logical*. <br> 要非常明理。 | 合乎邏輯的 |
| **liberal**[3] <br> 〔 ˈlɪbərəl 〕 adj. | *Liberal*. <br> 要開明。 | 開明的 |
| **liberty**[3] <br> 〔 ˈlɪbɚtɪ 〕 n. | Seek *liberty*. <br> 要追求自由。 | 自由 |
| **longevity**[6] <br> 〔 lɑnˈdʒɛvətɪ 〕 n. | Seek *longevity*. <br> 要追求長壽。 | 長壽 |

字首都是 lo

字尾是 al

是詞類變化

字尾是 ty

L

## I. 背景説明 :

想要快樂就要笑。*Laugh*. 可説成 : *Laugh* a lot.（要常笑。）（ = *Laugh often*.）Be a person who *laughs* frequently.（要做一個時常笑的人。）*Stay loose*. 字面的意思是「要保持鬆懈。」引申爲「要放鬆。」（ = *Be relaxed*.）可説成 : Stay calm and *loose*.（要保持冷靜和輕鬆。）（ = *Stay loose and calm*.）Stay *loose* and relaxed.（要保持輕鬆。）loose 的意思有 :「鬆的；不受束縛的；自由的」。*Fall in love*. 可説成 : *Fall in love* with somebody.（要和某人談戀愛。）*Fall in love* with something.（要愛上某個東西。）

*Be lovely*.（ = *Be a lovely person*.）*Be* a *lovely* and charming person.（要可愛又迷人。）*Lovable*. 在此指 Be *lovable*.（要討人喜歡。）（ = *Be a lovable person*.）Have a *lovable* character.（要有討人喜歡的個性。）*Very logical*. 在此指 Be *very logical*.（要非常明理。）（ = *Be a very logical person*.）Be a *very logical* thinker.（想法要非常合乎邏輯。）
【thinker（ˈθɪŋkɚ）*n*. 思想家；思考者】

*Liberal*. 在此指 Be *liberal*.（要開明。）Be a *liberal* thinker.（想法要開明。）Have a *liberal* outlook.（要有開明的看法。）*Seek liberty*.（ = *Seek freedom*.）*Seek liberty* and happiness.（要追求自由和快樂。）*Seek* peace and *liberty* for all.（要爲所有人尋求和平與自由。）（ = *Seek peace and freedom for everybody*.）*Seek* various *liberties*.（要追求各種自由。）*Seek longevity*. 可説成 : *Seek longevity* and health.（要追求長壽和健康。）（ = *Seek health and longevity*.）

## II. 英語演講：

### 【一字英語演講】

*My friends:*

*Laugh.*
*Stay loose.*
*Fall in love.*

*Be lovely.*
*Lovable.*
*Very logical.*

*Liberal.*
*Seek liberty.*
*Seek longevity.*

*This is what you*
*    need to be happy.*

### 【短篇英語演講】

*My friends:* 我的朋友們：

*Laugh* often. 要常笑。
*Stay loose* and relaxed. 要保持輕鬆。
*Fall in love* with something. 要愛上某個東西。

*Be a lovely* and charming person.
要可愛又迷人。
Be a *lovable* person. 要討人喜歡。
Be a *very logical* thinker. 想法要非常合乎邏輯。

Have a *liberal* outlook. 要有開明的想法。
*Seek liberty* and happiness. 要追求自由和快樂。
*Seek longevity* and health. 要追求長壽和健康。

*This is what you need to be happy.*
這就是快樂的必要條件。

## III. 短篇作文：

### What You Need to Be Happy

Here's what you need to be happy. *For starters*, be a person who *laughs* frequently. *Stay* calm and *loose*. *On the other hand*, *fall in love* with somebody. *Be a lovely* person. Have a *lovable* character. *However*, you also need to be a *very logical* person. Be a *liberal* thinker. *What's more*, *seek* peace and *liberty* for all. *In conclusion*, *seek longevity* and health, and you'll have what you need to be happy.

L

### 快樂的必要條件

　　以下就是快樂的必要條件。首先，要做一個時常笑的人。要保持冷靜和輕鬆。另一方面，要和某人談戀愛。要做一個可愛的人。要有討人喜歡的個性。然而，你也必須是一個非常明理的人。想法要開明。此外，要為所有人尋求和平與自由。總之，要追求長壽和健康，那你就會擁有快樂的必要條件。

　　\* *for starters* 首先　　character〔'kærɪktɚ〕*n.* 性格
　　*in conclusion* 總之

## IV. 填空：

　　____1____ often and you'll be happy for sure.  Similarly, stay ____2____ and relaxed.  And you haven't lived until you've fallen in ____3____ with something.

　　Additionally, be a ____4____ and charming person.  Be a ____5____ person.  You need to be a very ____6____ thinker.

　　All in all, simply have a ____7____ outlook.  Seek ____8____ and happiness.  Seek ____9____ and health, and you'll find happiness.

　　要常笑，那樣你當然就會快樂。同樣地，要保持輕鬆。而且直到你愛上某樣東西，你才算真正活過。

　　此外，要做一個可愛又迷人的人。要做一個討人喜歡的人。你的想法必須非常合乎邏輯。

　　總之，就是要有開明的看法。要追求自由和快樂。要追求長壽與健康，那樣你就會找到快樂。

【解答】1. Laugh　2. loose　3. love　4. lovely　5. lovable
　　　　6. logical　7. liberal　8. liberty　9. longevity

　　\* *for sure* 當然；確定　　similarly〔'sɪmələlɪ〕*adv.* 同樣地
　　*not…until* 直到～才…　　charming〔'tʃɑrmɪŋ〕*adj.* 迷人的
　　*all in all* 總之　　outlook〔'aut,luk〕*n.* 看法

## V. 詞彙題：

*Directions: Choose the one word that best completes the sentence.*

1. A well-adjusted person learns to _____ at his own mistakes.
   (A) lack　(B) launch　(C) laugh　(D) linger

2. When the big moment comes, stay _____ and relaxed.
   (A) loose　(B) literal　(C) literate　(D) latest

3. If you don't _____ your work, you're in the wrong profession.
   (A) lament　(B) lose　(C) limp　(D) love

4. A person with a _____ manner is rarely without company.
   (A) lengthy　(B) lovely　(C) lonely　(D) lousy

5. Your _____ personality will win friends and influence people.
   (A) lame　(B) latest　(C) likely　(D) loveable

6. Be a _____ thinker and you'll be able to solve any problem.
   (A) logical　(B) liable　(C) lunar　(D) local

7. A _____ and generous person is well-respected within the community.
   (A) lush　(B) lifelong　(C) liberal　(D) lyric

8. All people yearn for _____ and equality in society.
   (A) laundry　(B) liberty　(C) lullaby　(D) lobby

9. Let happiness be the secret to your _____.
   (A) luxury　(B) lottery　(C) longevity　(D) longitude

【答案】 1.( C )　2.( A )　3.( D )　4.( B )　5.( D )　6.( A )
　　　　 7.( C )　8.( B )　9.( C )

## VI. 同義字整理：

1. **laugh** 〔 læf 〕 *v.* 笑
   - = chuckle 〔'tʃʌkl̩ 〕
   - = giggle 〔'gɪgl̩ 〕

2. **loose** 〔 lus 〕 *adj.* 鬆的；不受束縛的；自由的
   - = unfettered 〔 ʌn'fɛtəd 〕
   - = unrestricted 〔ˌʌnrɪ'strɪktɪd 〕
   - = unconfined 〔ˌʌnkən'faɪnd 〕
   - = free 〔 fri 〕

3. **love** 〔 lʌv 〕 *n. v.* 愛
   - = adore 〔 ə'dor 〕
   - = treasure 〔'trɛʒə 〕
   - = cherish 〔'tʃɛrɪʃ 〕

   - = care for
   - = be attached to

4. **lovely** 〔'lʌvlɪ 〕 *adj.* 可愛的
   - = sweet 〔 swit 〕
   - = adorable 〔 ə'dorəbl̩ 〕

   - = appealing 〔 ə'pilɪŋ 〕
   - = attractive 〔 ə'træktɪv 〕

5. **lovable** 〔'lʌvəbl̩ 〕 *adj.* 可愛的；討人喜歡的
   - = charming 〔'tʃɑrmɪŋ 〕
   - = pleasing 〔'plizɪŋ 〕
   - = delightful 〔 dɪ'laɪtfəl 〕

6. **logical** 〔'lɑdʒɪkl̩ 〕 *adj.* 合乎邏輯的
   - = rational 〔'ræʃənl̩ 〕
   - = reasonable 〔'riznəbl̩ 〕
   - = coherent 〔 ko'hɪrənt 〕

   - = consistent 〔 kən'sɪstənt 〕
   - = well-organized 〔'wɛl'ɔrgənˌaɪzd 〕

7. **liberal** 〔'lɪbərəl 〕 *adj.* 開明的
   - = tolerant 〔'tɑlərənt 〕
   - = open-minded 〔'opən'maɪndɪd 〕
   - = permissive 〔 pə'mɪsɪv 〕
   - = easy-going 〔'iziˌgoɪŋ 〕

8. **liberty** 〔'lɪbətɪ 〕 *n.* 自由
   - = freedom 〔'fridəm 〕
   - = autonomy 〔 ɔ'tɑnəmɪ 〕
   - = independence 〔ˌɪndɪ'pɛndəns 〕
   - = self-determination 〔ˌsɛlf dɪˌtɜmɪ'neʃən 〕

9. **longevity** 〔 lɑn'dʒɛvətɪ 〕 *n.* 長壽；壽命
   - = long life
   - = great duration of life
   - = length or duration of life

**How to Be Happy**

# *13.* M

| 看英文唸出中文 | 一口氣說九句 | 看中文唸出英文 |
|---|---|---|
| **mingle**[5]　〔ˈmɪŋgl̩〕*v.* | 兩個動詞 *Mingle*. 要與人交際。 | 混合；交往；交際 |
| **marry**[1]　〔ˈmærɪ〕*v.* | *Marry*. 要結婚。 | 結婚  |
| **merry**[3]　〔ˈmɛrɪ〕*adj.* | Be *merry*. 要快樂。 | 歡樂的 |
| **mild**[4]　〔maɪld〕*adj.* | 三個形容詞 *Mild*. 要溫和。 | 溫和的 |
| **mature**[3]　〔məˈtʃʊr〕*adj.* | *Mature*. 要成熟。 | 成熟的 |
| **mellow**[6]　〔ˈmɛlo〕*adj.* | *Mellow*. 要放輕鬆。 | 成熟的；輕鬆愉快的 |
| **massage**[5]　〔məˈsɑʒ〕*n.* | 三個名詞 Have a *massage*. 要按摩。 | 按摩  |
| **meal**[2]　〔mil〕*n.* | A nice *meal*. 要吃一頓大餐。 | 一餐 |
| **movie**[1]　〔ˈmuvɪ〕*n.* | Watch a *movie*. 要看一場電影。 | 電影 |

M

## I. 背景説明：

　　*Mingle*. (＝*Socialize*.) Get out there and *mingle*. (要出去與人交際。) Don't be afraid to *mingle*. (不要害怕交際。) mingle 的意思有:「混合;交往;交際」。*Marry*. 可説成: *Marry* your soulmate. (要和你的知己結婚。) Get *married* to your sweetheart. (要和你心愛的人結婚。) *Be merry*. (要快樂。) (＝*Be happy*.) Be a *merry* soul. (要做一個快樂的人。) (＝*Be a merry person*.)【soul〔sol〕*n.* 人】

　　*Mild*. 在此指 Be *mild*. (要溫和。) (＝*Be a mild person*.) Have a *mild* character. (要有溫和的個性。) *Mature*. 在此指 Be *mature*. (要成熟。) (＝*Be a mature person*.) Have a *mature* outlook. (要有成熟的看法。) *Mellow*. 在此指 Be *mellow*. (要放輕鬆。) (＝*Be relaxed*.) Be a *mellow* person. (要做一個輕鬆愉快的人。) Have a *mellow* character. (要有隨和的個性。) (＝*Have an easy-going character*.) mellow 的主要意思是「成熟的」,但在這裡是指「輕鬆的」(relaxed)、「隨和的」(easy-going)、「平靜的」(calm)、「安詳的」(peaceful)。

　　*Have a massage*. (＝*Get a massage*.) Go for a Thai *massage*. (去做泰式按摩。) *A nice meal*. 在此指 Have *a nice meal*. (要吃一頓大餐。) (＝*Enjoy a nice meal*.) *Watch a movie*. 可説成: *Watch a movie* with friends. (要和朋友去看一場電影。) *Watch a* funny *movie*. (要看一部有趣的電影。)

**M**

## II. 英語演講：

### 【一字英語演講】

*My dearest students,*
*parents, and*
*teachers*:

*Mingle.*
*Marry.*
*Be merry.*

*Mild.*
*Mature.*
*Mellow.*

*Have a massage.*
*A nice meal.*
*Watch a movie.*

*Do this, and you can*
*be happy, too.*

### 【短篇英語演講】

*My dearest students, parents, and teachers:*
我最親愛的同學、家長，和老師：

Don't be afraid to *mingle*.　不要害怕與人交際。
Get *married* to your soulmate.
要和你的知己結婚。
*Be* a *merry* soul.　要做一個快樂的人。

Be a *mild* person.　要做一個溫和的人。
Have a *mature* outlook.　要有成熟的看法。
Have a *mellow* character.　要有隨和的個性。

*Have a* Thai *massage*.　要去做泰式按摩。
Have *a nice meal*.　要吃一頓大餐。
*Watch a movie* with friends.
要和朋友去看一場電影。

*Do this, and you can be happy, too.*
這麼做，你也會快樂。

## III. 短篇作文：

### You Can Be Happy, Too

　　Happiness is a complicated thing.　*For sure*, everybody wants to be happy, but how?　You can be happy, too, if you follow this advice.　*First*, get out there and *mingle*.　Get *married* to your sweetheart.　*Be* a *merry* and jolly person.　*Second*, have a *mild* character.　Be a *mature* person.　Be a *mellow* person.　*Additionally*, *have a massage*.　Enjoy *a nice meal*.　*Without a doubt*, *watch a* funny *movie* and you can be happy, too.

**M**

### 你也會快樂

快樂是一件很複雜的事。當然，每個人都想要快樂，但要怎麼做？如果你聽從這些建議，你也會快樂。首先，要出去與人交際。要和你心愛的人結婚。要做一個非常快樂的人。其次，要有溫和的個性。要做一個成熟的人。要做一個輕鬆愉快的人。此外，要按摩。要吃一頓大餐。無疑地，看一部好笑的電影，你也會很快樂。

* complicated〔ˋkamplə͵ketɪd〕*adj.* 複雜的　　follow〔ˋfɑlo〕*v.* 聽從
jolly〔ˋdʒɑlɪ〕*adj.* 高興的　***without a doubt*** 無疑地

## IV. 填空：

In the beginning, don't be afraid to ___1___. Get ___2___ to your soulmate. Be a ___3___ and jolly soul who spreads goodwill.

Likewise, be a ___4___ and consistently happy person. Have a ___5___ outlook. Have a smooth and ___6___ character.

Finally, treat yourself to a one-hour Thai ___7___. Then, have a nice ___8___. Watch a ___9___ with friends and you can be happy, too.

首先，不要害怕交際。要和你的知己結婚。要做一個散播善意，非常快樂的人。

同樣地，要做一個溫和而且一直都很快樂的人。要有成熟的看法。要有圓滑而且隨和的個性。

最後，要招待自己去做一小時的泰式按摩。然後，要吃一頓大餐。要和朋友去看一場電影，那樣你也會很快樂。

**【解答】** 1. mingle　2. married　3. merry　4. mild　5. mature
　　　　　6. mellow　7. massage　8. meal　9. movie
　　* soulmate〔ˋsol͵met〕*n.* 知己　　goodwill〔ˋgʊd͵wɪl〕*n.* 善意
　　likewise〔ˋlaɪk͵waɪz〕*adv.* 同樣地
　　consistently〔kənˋsɪstəntlɪ〕*adv.* 經常；一直
　　smooth〔smuð〕*adj.* 圓滑的　　treat〔trit〕*v.* 招待

**M**

## V. 詞彙題：

***Directions:*** *Choose the one word that best completes the sentence.*

1. Parties are more fun if you _____ with other guests.
   (A) minimize   (B) mislead   (C) mingle   (D) manage

2. If you _____ the right person, you'll be happy forever.
   (A) modify   (B) meditate   (C) memorize   (D) marry

3. Everybody wants to hang out with a _____ character.
   (A) merry   (B) massive   (C) melancholy   (D) medieval

4. Your _____ personality will attract many followers.
   (A) miserable   (B) minimal   (C) mild   (D) mental

5. Start making _____ decisions and you'll definitely be happy.
   (A) marine   (B) mature   (C) missing   (D) moist

6. Be a _____ person and take the easy way through life.
   (A) militant   (B) marginal   (C) martial   (D) mellow

7. If you're tired and sore, a _____ will feel great.
   (A) message   (B) massage   (C) massacre   (D) messenger

8. Treat yourself to a big, expensive _____ sometime.
   (A) media   (B) mail   (C) meal   (D) mall

9. Rent a _____, make some popcorn, and enjoy the night.
   (A) movie   (B) mode   (C) mower   (D) motor

**M**

【答案】 1.（C）　2.（D）　3.（A）　4.（C）　5.（B）　6.（D）
　　　　 7.（B）　8.（C）　9.（A）

## VI. 同義字整理：

1. **mingle** (ˈmɪŋg!) *v.* 混合；
 交際；交往
  = socialize (ˈsoʃəlˌaɪz)
  = associate (əˈsoʃɪˌet)
  = circulate (ˈsɝkjəˌlet)
  = hang out

2. **marry** (ˈmærɪ) *v.* 結婚
  = wed (wɛd)
  = tie the knot
  = become man and wife

3. **merry** (ˈmɛrɪ) *adj.* 歡樂的
  = happy (ˈhæpɪ)
  = jolly (ˈdʒɑlɪ)
  = glad (glæd)
  = cheerful (ˈtʃɪrfəl)
  = festive (ˈfɛstɪv)

4. **mild** (maɪld) *adj.* 溫和的
  = gentle (ˈdʒɛnt!)
  = pleasant (ˈplɛznt)
  = mellow (ˈmɛlo)
  = easy-going (ˈizɪˌgoɪŋ)

5. **mature** (məˈtʃʊr) *adj.* 成熟的
  = adult (əˈdʌlt)
  = wise (waɪz)
  = sensible (ˈsɛnsəb!)
  = experienced (ɪkˈspɪrɪənst)
  = responsible (rɪˈspɑnsəb!)

6. **mellow** (ˈmɛlo) *adj.* 成熟的；
 輕鬆愉快的；隨和的
  = relaxed (rɪˈlækst)
  = easy-going (ˈizɪˌgoɪŋ)
  = pleasant (ˈplɛznt)

7. **massage** (məˈsɑʒ) *n.* 按摩
  = rub-down (ˈrʌbˌdaʊn)
  = rubbing (ˈrʌbɪŋ)
  = the rubbing or kneading of
   parts of the body to relax the
   muscles, aid circulation, or
   provide sensual pleasure

8. **meal** (mil) *n.* 一餐
  = dinner (ˈdɪnə)
  = feast (fist)
  = banquet (ˈbæŋkwɪt)

9. **movie** (ˈmuvɪ) *n.* 電影
  = film (fɪlm)
  = motion picture
  = moving picture

**M**

**How to Be Happy**

# *14.* N

| 看英文唸出中文 | 一口氣説九句 | 看中文唸出英文 |
|---|---|---|

**natural**[2]
('nætʃərəl ) *adj.*

**naughty**[2]
('nɔtɪ ) *adj.*

**naive**[5]
( nɑ'iv ) *adj.*

字首都是 na

Be *natural*.
要自然。　　　　　自然的

*Naughty*.
要頑皮。　　　　　頑皮的

*Naive*.
要天眞。　　　　　天眞的

---

**novel**[2]
('nɑvl̩ ) *n.*

**nap**[3]
( næp ) *n.*

兩個名詞

Read a *novel*.
要看一本小說。　　小說

Take a *nap*.
要小睡片刻。　　　小睡

**nutritiously**[6]
( nju'trɪʃəslɪ ) *adv.*

Eat *nutritiously*.
要吃營養的食物。　營養地

---

**nerve**[3]
( nɝv ) *n.*

Have lots of *nerve*.
要很有勇氣。　　　神經；勇氣

**numerous**[4]
('njumərəs ) *adj.*

*Numerous* friends.
要有無數的朋友。　非常多的

**neighborhood**[3]
('nebɚ͵hud ) *n.*

Explore the
*neighborhood*.
要去探索鄰近地區。　鄰近地區

**N**

## I. 背景説明：

*Be natural.* ( = *Be a natural person.* ) Have a genuine and *natural* personality. (要有眞誠又自然的個性。) *Naughty.* 在此指 Be *naughty.* (要頑皮。) ( = *Be mischievous.* ) Be *naughty* once in a while. (偶爾要頑皮一下。) It's OK to be *naughty* sometimes. (有時候頑皮一下沒關係。) *Naive.* 在此指 Be *naive.* (要天眞。) ( = *Be innocent.* ) Be a *naive* person. (要做一個天眞的人。) Maintain a *naive* character. (要保持天眞的個性。)

*Read a novel.* 可說成：*Read a* new *novel.* (要看一本新的小說。) *Read a* mystery *novel.* (要看一本偵探小說。) 【mystery〔'mɪstrɪ〕*adj.* 神祕的　*n.* 偵探小說】*Take a nap.* 可說成：*Take a* short *nap.* (要小睡一下。) Enjoy an afternoon *nap.* (要睡個午覺。) *Eat nutritiously.* 可說成：Always *eat nutritiously.* (一定要吃有營養的食物。) Try to *eat nutritiously.* (要儘量吃有營養的食物。)

*Have lots of nerve.* (要很有勇氣。) ( = *Be courageous.* ) Have the *nerve* to try new things. (要有勇氣嘗試新事物。) Have enough *nerve* to be daring. (要有足夠的勇氣大膽做事。) nerve 的主要意思是「神經」，在此作「勇氣」解。*Numerous friends.* 在此指 Have *numerous friends.* (要有無數的朋友。) ( = *Have many friends.* ) Have as many friends as possible. (能有多少朋友，就要有多少朋友。) *Explore the neighborhood.* 可說成：Explore your *neighborhood.* (要去你家附近逛逛。) Explore other *neighborhoods.* (要去其他地方逛逛。)

## II. 英語演講：

### 【一字英語演講】

*Hello*, *friends*:

*Be natural.*
*Naughty.*
*Naive.*

*Read a novel.*
*Take a nap.*
*Eat nutritiously.*

*Have lots of nerve.*
*Numerous friends.*
*Explore the*
　*neighborhood.*

*These are some*
　*secrets of happiness.*

### 【短篇英語演講】

*Hello*, *friends*: 哈囉，朋友們：

Always *be natural*. 一定要自然。
It's OK to be *naughty* sometimes.
有時候頑皮一下沒關係。
Maintain a *naive* character. 要保持天眞的個性。

*Read a* mystery *novel*. 要看一本偵探小說。
*Take a nap* every day. 每天都要睡個午覺。
Try to *eat nutritiously*. 要儘量吃有營養的食物。

*Have lots of nerve* when times are tough.
在艱難的時候，要很有勇氣。
Have *numerous friends*. 要有無數的朋友。
Get out and *explore the neighborhood*.
要出去到你家附近逛逛。

*These are some secrets of happiness*.
這就是一些快樂的祕訣。

## III. 短篇作文：

### Secrets of Happiness

　　Do you wish to know the secrets of happiness? Well, you're in luck. *For one thing*, *be* a *natural* and easy-going person. *On the other hand*, be *naughty* once in a while. *Meanwhile*, be a *naive* person. *Read a* new *novel*. *Take a* short *nap*. *On top of that*, always *eat nutritiously*. *Have* enough *nerve* to be daring. Have *numerous friends*. *Finally*, *explore* other *neighborhoods* and discover the secret of happiness.

N

### 快樂的祕訣

你希望知道快樂的祕訣嗎？嗯，你很幸運。首先，要做一個自然而且隨和的人。另一方面，偶爾要頑皮一下。同時，要做一個天眞的人。要看一本新的小說。要小睡一下。此外，一定要吃有營養的東西。要有足夠的勇氣大膽做事。要有無數的朋友。最後，要去其他地方逛逛，並且發現快樂的祕訣。

* *in luck* 幸運　　*for one thing* 首先
easy-going〔ˈizɪˌgoɪŋ〕*adj.* 隨和的；悠哉的　　*once in a while* 偶爾
*on top of that* 此外　　daring〔ˈdɛrɪŋ〕*adj.* 勇敢的

## IV. 填空：

First, have a genuine and ___1___ personality.  Conversely, it's OK to be ___2___ sometimes.  But of course, maintain a ___3___ character.

Additionally, read a couple of mystery ___4___.  Enjoy an afternoon ___5___.  But remember to eat ___6___ and stay healthy.

What's more, have the ___7___ to try new things.  Have ___8___ friends.  Most importantly, explore your ___9___ and find the secret to happiness.

首先，要有眞誠又自然的個性。相反地，有時候頑皮一下沒關係。但是，當然要保持天眞的個性。

此外，要看幾本偵探小說。要睡個午覺。但要記得吃有營養的食物，並保持健康。

而且，要有勇氣嘗試新事物。要有無數的朋友。最重要的是，要到你家附近去逛逛，並找到快樂的祕訣。

【解答】1. natural　2. naughty　3. naive　4. novels　5. nap
　　　　6. nutritiously　7. nerve　8. numerous　9. neighborhood
　　* genuine〔ˈdʒɛnjʊɪn〕*adj.* 眞的
　　　conversely〔kənˈvɝslɪ〕*adv.* 相反地　　explore〔ɪkˈsplor〕*v.* 探索

## V. 詞彙題：

*Directions: Choose the one word that best completes the sentence.*

1. It's very easy to be a _____ person; just be yourself.
   (A) notorious   (B) naval   (C) natural   (D) national

2. Everybody needs to be _____ every now and then.
   (A) naughty   (B) nasty   (C) negative   (D) narrative

3. A _____ attitude will keep your mind free of worry.
   (A) noticeable   (B) needy   (C) native   (D) naive

4. Reading a _____ is like meeting and getting to know a
   new friend.
   (A) notebook   (B) nuisance   (C) novel   (D) needle

5. If you're having a rough day, take a _____ in the afternoon.
   (A) net   (B) nap   (C) neck   (D) nest

6. Nothing is more important than eating _____.
   (A) nevertheless   (B) nervously   (C) namely   (D) nutritiously

7. It takes a lot of _____ to get out of your comfort zone and
   try something new.
   (A) nerve   (B) necessity   (C) network   (D) noise

8. You will have _____ opportunities to discover happiness.
   (A) nuclear   (B) noble   (C) numerous   (D) normal

9. Go find some hidden treasures in your _____.
   (A) nursery   (B) neighborhood   (C) nickname   (D) nightmare

【答案】 1.( C )   2.( A )   3.( D )   4.( C )   5.( B )   6.( D )
            7.( A )   8.( C )   9.( B )

N

## VI. 同義字整理：

1. **natural** (ˈnætʃərəl ) *adj.*
   自然的
   - = real (ˈriəl )
   - = genuine (ˈdʒɛnjuɪn )
   - = unaffected (ˌʌnəˈfɛktɪd )

2. **naughty** (ˈnɔtɪ ) *adj.* 頑皮的
   - = playful (ˈplefəl )
   - = mischievous (ˈmɪstʃɪvəs )

3. **naive** ( nɑˈiv ) *adj.* 天真的
   - = simple (ˈsɪmpḷ )
   - = childlike (ˈtʃaɪldˌlaɪk )
   - = innocent (ˈɪnəsṇt )

4. **novel** (ˈnɑvḷ ) *n.* 小說
   - = story (ˈstorɪ )
   - = tale ( tel )
   - = fiction (ˈfɪkʃən )
   - = narrative (ˈnærətɪv )

5. **nap** ( næp ) *n.* 小睡
   - = rest ( rɛst )
   - = sleep ( slip )
   - = catnap (ˈkætˌnæp )
   - = forty winks

6. **nutritiously** ( njuˈtrɪʃəslɪ )
   *adv.* 營養地
   - = beneficially (ˌbɛnəˈfɪʃəlɪ )
   - = healthfully (ˈhɛlθfəlɪ )
   - = wholesomely (ˈholsəmlɪ )

7. **nerve** ( nɜv ) *n.* 神經；勇氣
   - = bravery (ˈbrevərɪ )
   - = courage (ˈkɜɪdʒ )
   - = daring (ˈdɛrɪŋ )
   - = determination ( dɪˌtɜməˈneʃən )

8. **numerous** (ˈnjumərəs ) *adj.*
   非常多的
   - = many (ˈmɛnɪ )
   - = countless (ˈkauntlɪs )
   - = abundant ( əˈbʌndənt )
   - = innumerable ( ɪˈnjumərəbḷ )

9. **neighborhood** (ˈnebəˌhud ) *n.*
   鄰近地區
   - = area (ˈɛrɪə )
   - = district (ˈdɪstrɪkt )
   - = region (ˈridʒən )
   - = environment ( ɪnˈvaɪrənmənt )

**How to Be Happy**

# *15.* O

O

| 看英文唸出中文 | 一口氣說九句 | 看中文唸出英文 |
|---|---|---|
| **organic**[4] ﹝ɔrˈɡænɪk﹞ *adj.* | Eat *organic*. 要吃有機食物。 | 有機的 |
| **oyster**[5] ﹝ˈɔɪstɚ﹞ *n.* | *Oysters*. 要吃生蠔。 | 生蠔 |
| **olive**[5] ﹝ˈɑlɪv﹞ *n.* | *Olives*. 要吃橄欖。 | 橄欖 |

（三種食物）

---

| **outdoors**[3] ﹝ˈaʊtˈdorz﹞ *adv.* | Go *outdoors*. 要去戶外。 | 在戶外 |
| **outing**[6] ﹝ˈaʊtɪŋ﹞ *n.* | On an *outing*. 要去郊遊。 | 郊遊 |
| **overseas**[2] ﹝ˈovɚˈsiz﹞ *adv.* | Travel *overseas*. 要出國旅行。 | 在海外 |

（字首是 out）

---

| **outfit**[6] ﹝ˈaʊtˌfɪt﹞ *n.* | Buy an *outfit*. 要買衣服。 | 服裝 |
| **outlet**[6] ﹝ˈaʊtˌlɛt﹞ *n.* | Hit an *outlet* store. 要去名牌折扣店。 | 名牌折扣店 |
| **outside**[1] ﹝aʊtˈsaɪd﹞ *prep.* | Think *outside* the box. 要跳脫框架思考。 | 在…的外面 |

（字首是 out）

## I. 背景説明：

*Eat organic.*（要吃有機食物。）（ = *Eat organic food.* ）eat 後面常加形容詞，形成慣用句。Buy *organic* products.（要買有機的產品。）吃有機食物可以避免吃到殺蟲劑。全世界有一百七十多種殺蟲劑，吃了會引起癌症、過敏，或自體免疫相關的疾病。*Oysters.* 在此指 Eat *oysters.*（要吃生蠔。）可説成：Have some *oysters.*（要吃一些生蠔。）Enjoy a serving of *oysters.*（要享用一份生蠔。）【serving〔'sɜvɪŋ〕 *n.* 一份】吃生蠔可以提高免疫力，強肝解毒，有助於睡眠。*Olives.* 在此指 Eat *olives.*（要吃橄欖。）可説成：Eat some *olives.*（要吃一些橄欖。）Enjoy some tasty *olives.*（要享用一些美味的橄欖。）吃橄欖可以抗衰老、防癌，清肺利咽。

oyster

olive

*Go outdoors.* 可説成：*Go outdoors* and get some fresh air.（要到戶外呼吸一些新鮮的空氣。）戶外空氣比室內好八倍，到戶外會使人快樂。Spend as much time *outdoors* as possible.（儘可能多花時間到戶外。）*On an outing.* 在此指 Go *on an outing.*（要去郊遊。）Enjoy an afternoon *outing.*（要享受一個下午的郊遊。）*Travel overseas.* 可説成：*Travel overseas* frequently.（要常出國旅行。）Travel to many *overseas* destinations.（要到許多海外的地方旅行。）【在此 overseas 是形容詞，作「海外的」解。】

　　***Buy an outfit.*** 可說成：Buy some new clothes.（要買一些新衣服。）***Buy a*** new ***outfit.***（要買新衣服。）Get yourself a fancy new ***outfit.***（給自己買一件漂亮的新衣服。）***Hit an outlet store.*** 可說成：Go to ***an outlet store.***（要去名牌折扣店。）(*= Visit an outlet store.*) outlet 的意思有：「經銷點；商店；(情感的)發洩途徑；出口；出水口；排氣口；電源插座」。***Think outside the box.*** 字面的意思是「要在盒子的外面思考。」引申為「要跳脫框架思考。」這是慣用句，意思是「想法要不落俗套。」(*= Think something that is outside of or beyond what is considered usual, traditional, or conventional.*) 也就是「想法要創新。」(*= Think creatively and innovatively.*) ***Think outside the box*** to find a better solution.（要跳脫框架思考，以找到更好的解決之道。）Good ideas come when you ***think outside the box.***（當你跳脫框架思考時，就會有好的點子出現。）【solution〔səˋluʃən〕*n.* 解決之道】

## II. 英語演講：

| 【一字英語演講】 | 【短篇英語演講】 |
|---|---|
| *Boys and girls of all ages:* | *Boys and girls of all ages:* 各位男孩、各位女孩： |
| *Eat organic.* | *Eat organic* food. 要吃有機食物。 |
| *Oysters.* | Have some *oysters*. 要吃一些生蠔。 |
| *Olives.* | Eat some *olives*. 要吃一些橄欖。 |
| *Go outdoors.* | *Go outdoors* and get some fresh air. 要到戶外呼吸一些新鮮的空氣。 |
| *On an outing.* | Enjoy nature *on an outing*. 郊遊時好好享受大自然。 |
| *Travel overseas.* | *Travel overseas* frequently. 要常常出國旅行。 |
| *Buy an outfit.* | *Buy a* new *outfit*. 要買新衣服。 |
| *Hit an outlet store.* | *Hit an outlet store* with friends. 要和朋友去名牌折扣店。 |
| *Think outside the box.* | *Think outside the box* to find a better solution. 要跳脫框架思考，以找到更好的解決之道。 |
| *Do this, and you'll find your happiness.* | *Do this, and you'll find your happiness.* 這麼做，你就會找到你的快樂。 |

## III. 短篇作文：

### Find Your Happiness

Happiness is everywhere if you're looking for it. Here's a good place to start. *First of all*, buy *organic* products. Enjoy a serving of *oysters*. Enjoy some tasty *olives*. *On the other hand*, spend as much time *outdoors* as possible. Plan an *outing* to the countryside. Travel to many *overseas* destinations. *Meanwhile*, get yourself a fancy new *outfit*. *Hit an outlet store*. *But more importantly*, good ideas come when you *think outside the box*, and that's where you will find your happiness.

### 找到你的快樂

如果你正在尋找快樂,快樂無所不在。這裡有一個好的起點。首先,要買有機的產品。要享用一份生蠔。要享用一些美味的橄欖。另一方面,盡可能多花時間到戶外。要規劃到鄉下郊遊。要到許多海外的地方旅行。同時,要替自己買一件漂亮的新衣服。要去名牌折扣店。但更重要的是,當你跳脫框架思考時,就會有好的點子出現,那你就能找到你的快樂。

* tasty〔'testɪ〕*adj.* 好吃的
  countryside〔'kʌntrɪ,saɪd〕*n.* 鄉村地區
  destination〔,dɛstə'neʃən〕*n.* 目的地　　fancy〔'fænsɪ〕*adj.* 華麗的

## IV. 填空:

To begin with, buy, prepare, and eat ___1___ food. Besides, have a big serving of ___2___. Eat some ___3___.

Meanwhile, go ___4___ and get some fresh air. Enjoy an afternoon ___5___ with friends. And of course, travel ___6___ frequently.

On top of that, buy a new ___7___. Go shopping at an ___8___ store. Above all, think ___9___ the box, to find a better solution—and your happiness.

首先,要購買、準備,並且吃有機的食物。此外,要吃一大份生蠔。要吃一些橄欖。

同時,要去戶外呼吸一些新鮮的空氣。要和朋友享受一個下午的郊遊。而且,當然要經常出國旅遊。

還有,要買一件新衣服。要去名牌折扣店購物。最重要的是,要跳脫框架思考,以找到更好的解決之道——以及你的快樂。

【解答】1. organic　2. oysters　3. olives　4. outdoors　5. outing
6. overseas　7. outfit　8. outlet　9. outside

## V. 詞彙題：

**Directions:** *Choose the one word that best completes the sentence.*

1. Most of the major supermarkets have a section for _____ foods.
   (A) obscure　(B) oblong　(C) offensive　(D) organic

2. _____ are one of the most popular types of seafood.
   (A) Oysters　(B) Onions　(C) Organs　(D) Oatmeal

3. _____ are delicious if eaten alone or prepared with another ingredient.
   (A) Oaks　(B) Oars　(C) Olives　(D) Orbits

4. The problem with kids today is they don't spend enough time _____.
   (A) outwards　(B) outdoors　(C) odds　(D) origins

5. Plan an _____ with your friends on a nice summer day.
   (A) outlaw　(B) octopus　(C) option　(D) outing

6. Many people enjoy traveling _____.
   (A) overpass　(B) overall　(C) overseas　(D) overhead

7. A new _____ will totally change your attitude.
   (A) ocean　(B) outfit　(C) outrage　(D) ozone

8. There are lots of good bargains at the _____ store.
   (A) outlet　(B) outline　(C) outlook　(D) outright

9. To solve a tough problem, think _____ the box.
   (A) off　(B) onto　(C) outside　(D) over

【答案】1.（D）　2.（A）　3.（C）　4.（B）　5.（D）　6.（C）
　　　　7.（B）　8.（A）　9.（C）

## VI. 同義字整理：

**1. organic** 〔 ɔr'gænɪk 〕 *adj.* 有機的

- = natural 〔'nætʃərəl 〕
- = additive-free 〔'ædətɪv'fri 〕
- = chemical-free 〔'kɛmɪkḷ'fri 〕
- = pesticide-free 〔'pɛstə,saɪd'fri 〕

**2. oyster** 〔'ɔɪstɚ 〕 *n.* 生蠔

- = any of several edible bivalve mollusks of the family Ostreidae, having a rough, irregularly shaped shell attached to the substrate in shallow marine waters

**3. olive** 〔'ɑlɪv 〕 *n.* 橄欖

- = the small oval fruit of an olive tree, usually changing in color from green to black as it ripens, used for food and as a source of oil

**4. outdoors** 〔'aut'dorz 〕 *adv.* 在戶外

- = out-of-doors
- = outside 〔'aut'saɪd 〕
- = open air

**5. outing** 〔'autɪŋ 〕 *n.* 郊遊

- = trip 〔 trɪp 〕
- = journey 〔'dʒɝnɪ 〕
- = expedition 〔,ɛkspɪ'dɪʃən 〕
- = spin 〔 spɪn 〕
- = excursion 〔 ɪk'skɝʒən 〕

**6. overseas** 〔'ovɚ'siz 〕 *adv.* 在海外

- = abroad 〔 ə'brɔd 〕
- = out of the country
- = in foreign lands

**7. outfit** 〔'aut,fɪt 〕 *n.* 服裝

- = dress 〔 drɛs 〕
- = clothes 〔 kloz 〕
- = costume 〔'kɑstjum 〕
- = attire 〔 ə'taɪr 〕
- = apparel 〔 ə'pærəl 〕

**8. outlet** 〔'aut,lɛt 〕 *n.* 名牌折扣店

- = discount store
- = discount house
- = wholesale house

**9. outside** 〔 aut'saɪd 〕 *prep.* 在…的外面

- = outside of
- = beyond 〔 bɪ'jɑnd 〕
- = without 〔 wɪð'aut 〕

**How to Be Happy**

# *16.* P (1)

| 看英文唸出中文 | 一口氣説九句 | 看中文唸出英文 |
|---|---|---|
| **paint**¹<br>〔 pent 〕 *v.* | 字首是Pa *Paint.*<br>要畫畫。 | 畫 |
| **party**¹<br>〔'partɪ 〕 *v.* | *Party.*<br>要去玩。 | 盡情狂歡 |
| **pleasure**²<br>〔'plɛʒɚ 〕 *n.* | Seek *pleasure.*<br>要尋找樂趣。 | 樂趣 |
| **present**²<br>〔'prɛznt 〕 *adj.* | Be *present.*<br>要活在當下。 | 現在的 |
| **playful**²<br>〔'plefəl 〕 *adj.* | 三個形容詞 *Playful.*<br>要愛玩。 字尾是ful | 愛玩的 |
| **peaceful**²<br>〔'pisfəl 〕 *adj.* | Very *peaceful.*<br>要非常平靜。 | 和平的 |
| **partner**²<br>〔'partnɚ 〕 *n.* | Find a *partner.*<br>要找個夥伴。 字首是pa | 夥伴 |
| **pastime**⁵<br>〔'pæs,taɪm 〕 *n.* | 三個名詞 *Pastime.*<br>要找個消遣。 | 消遣 |
| **pet**¹<br>〔 pɛt 〕 *n.* | *Pet.*<br>要找隻寵物。 | 寵物 |

## I. 背景說明：

paint 和 draw 不一樣，paint 是用畫筆（brush），有點像塗油漆一樣；draw 是用鉛筆、鋼筆、原子筆來畫。*Paint*. 可說成：*Paint* a landscape.（要畫風景。）*Paint* a portrait.（要畫肖像畫。）

【landscape〔'lændskep〕*n.* 風景　　portrait〔'portret〕*n.* 肖像畫】

**P**

paint a landscape

paint a portrait

*Party*. 可說成：Let's *party*.（我們去玩吧。）在口語中，party 當動詞很常用。

> Let's *party*.（我們好好玩一下吧。）
> = Let's celebrate.（我們慶祝一下吧。）
> = Let's have fun.（我們去玩吧。）
> = Let's have a good time.（我們去玩吧。）
> = Let's enjoy ourselves.（我們享受一下吧。）

*Party* tonight.（今天晚上要去狂歡。）Let's *party* this weekend.（我們這個週末去狂歡一下吧。）party 也可以當名詞，作「聚會；派對」解，如 Have a *party*.（要舉辦派對。）( = *Throw a party*. ) party 不一定指「舞會」，一群人聚在一起，吃點東西，都稱作 party。
*Seek pleasure*. ( = *Seek enjoyment*. ) *Seek pleasure* in life.（要尋找人生的樂趣。）( = *Seek pleasure in your life*. ) Always be in search of *pleasure*.（要一直尋找樂趣。）【*in search of* 尋找】

> *Be present.*（要活在當下。）( = *Seize the moment.* )
>
> > **Be present.**
> >
> { = Be in the moment.（要活在當下。）
> { = Be awake.（要清醒。）
> { = Be alert.（要有警覺。）

**Be present.** 的意思是「不要想到未來，只想此時此地。」( = *Don't think about the future but focus on here and now.* ) present 作「出席的」解時，多用於過去式，如：How many people were **present** at the meeting?（有多少人出席那場會議？）這裡的 **Be present.** 不能作「要出席。」解。Be a **present** person.（要做個有警覺的人。）( = *Be an alert person.* ) Be **present** and alive in the moment.（要活在當下。）( = *Be alert and focused on what you are doing.* ) *Playful.* 在此指 Be *playful*.（要愛玩。）( = *Be a playful person.* ) Have a **playful** personality.（要有愛玩的個性。） *Very peaceful.* 在此指 Be *very peaceful*.（要非常平靜。）( = *Be very calm.* ) Be a **very peaceful** person.（要做一個非常平靜的人。）

　　**Find a partner.** ( = *Find a mate.* ) **Find a** life **partner**.（要找一個終生的夥伴。）**Find an** activity **partner**.（要找一個一起做事的夥伴。）( = *Find someone to do things with.* ) *Pastime.* 在此指 Find a *pastime*.（要找個消遣。）( = *Find a hobby.* 要找個嗜好。）Find an enjoyable **pastime**.（要找一個令人愉快的消遣。）Entertain yourself with a **pastime**.（要從事消遣娛樂自己。）pastime 的意思有：「消遣；娛樂；嗜好」。*Pet.* 在此指 Find a *pet*.（要找隻寵物。）可說成：Own a *pet*.（要養一隻寵物。）Adopt a *pet*.（要領養一隻寵物。）【adopt〔ə'dɑpt〕v. 領養】

## II. 英語演講：

| 【一字英語演講】 | 【短篇英語演講】 |
|---|---|
| *Hey, guys:* | *Hey, guys:* 嘿，大家好： |
| *Paint.* | *Paint* a landscape. 要畫風景。 |
| *Party.* | Throw a *party*. 要舉辦派對。 |
| *Seek pleasure.* | *Seek pleasure* in life. 要尋找人生的樂趣。 |
| *Be present.* | *Be* a *present* person. 要做個有警覺的人。 |
| *Playful.* | Have a *playful* personality. 要有愛玩的個性。 |
| *Very peaceful.* | Be a *very peaceful* person. 要做一個非常平靜的人。 |
| *Find a partner.* | *Find an* activity *partner*. |
| *Pastime.* | 要找一個一起做事的夥伴。 |
| *Pet.* | Entertain yourself with a *pastime*. |
| | 要從事消遣娛樂自己。 |
| *This is how to get more happiness in your life.* | Adopt a *pet*. 要領導一隻寵物。 |
| | *This is how to get more happiness in your life.* |
| | 這就是如何在生活中獲得更多快樂的方法。 |

## III. 短篇作文：

### Get More Happiness in Your Life

I know you want more happiness in your life. Here's how:
*First of all*, *paint* a portrait. Have a *party*. Always be in search of
*pleasure*. *Meanwhile*, *be present* and alive in the moment. Be a
*playful* person. *On the other hand*, be *very* calm and *peaceful*.
*Find a* life *partner*. Find an enjoyable *pastime*. *And finally*, owning
a *pet* will certainly put more happiness in your life. Try it.

### 要在生活中獲得更多的快樂

　　我知道你想在生活中有更多的快樂。方法如下：首先，要畫肖像畫。要舉辦派對。要一直尋找樂趣。同時，要活在當下。要做一個愛玩的人。另一方面，要非常冷靜而且平靜。要找一個終生的夥伴。要找一個令人愉快的消遣。最後，養一隻寵物一定能使你的生活更快樂。試試看吧。

* alive〔əˋlaɪv〕*adj.* 活的；精力充沛的　　***the moment*** 此刻；現在
  enjoyable〔ɪnˋdʒɔɪəbl̩〕*adj.* 令人愉快的

## IV. 填空：

　　When you need to get more happiness in your life, ___1___ a landscape. Or, throw a ___2___. Most of all, be a person who seeks ___3___ in life.

　　In a similar fashion, be a ___4___ person. Have a ___5___ and fun-loving personality. Be a very ___6___ person.

　　Besides, find an activity ___7___. Entertain yourself with a ___8___. Go to the animal shelter and adopt a ___9___.

　　當你需要在生活中得到更多快樂時，要畫風景畫。或者，舉辦一場派對。最重要的是，要做一個會尋找人生樂趣的人。

　　同樣地，要做個有警覺的人。要有愛玩又風趣的個性。要做一個非常平靜的人。

　　此外，要找一個一起做事的夥伴。要從事消遣娛樂自己。要去動物收容所領養一隻寵物。

【解答】 1. paint　2. party　3. pleasure　4. present　5. playful
　　　　 6. peaceful　7. partner　8. pastime　9. pet
　　　　 * throw〔θro〕*v.* 舉行　　fashion〔ˋfæʃən〕*n.* 方式；作風
　　　　 ***in a similar fashion*** 同樣地
　　　　 fun-loving〔ˋfʌnˏlʌvɪŋ〕*adj.* 風趣的
　　　　 shelter〔ˋʃɛltɚ〕*n.* 收容所

## V. 詞彙題：

***Directions:*** *Choose the one word that best completes the sentence.*

1. You will enjoy a sense of accomplishment by _____ a picture.
   (A) painting　(B) pardoning　(C) paralyzing　(D) persuading

2. Sometimes, you just have to say, "Let's _____!"
   (A) puzzle　(B) panic　(C) party　(D) pretend

3. There are a million different ways to add _____ to your life.
   (A) pottery　(B) pleasure　(C) plague　(D) posture

4. Don't think about the future but focus on the _____.
   (A) pious　(B) private　(C) pacific　(D) present

5. Develop a keen sense of when it's appropriate to be _____.
   (A) plastic　(B) pathetic　(C) playful　(D) painful

6. Everybody on Earth deserves to live a _____ existence.
   (A) peaceful　(B) parallel　(C) passive　(D) partial

7. Find an activity _____ to do things with.
   (A) pedestrian　(B) peasant　(C) passenger　(D) partner

8. The older you get, the more important a _____ becomes.
   (A) pavement　(B) pastime　(C) parachute　(D) phrase

9. There are thousands of abandoned _____ needing a good home right now.
   (A) pistols　(B) penguins　(C) pets　(D) pandas

【答案】 1.（A）　2.（C）　3.（B）　4.（D）　5.（C）　6.（A）
　　　　 7.（D）　8.（B）　9.（C）

## VI. 同義字整理：

1. **paint** 〔 pent 〕 *v.* 畫

   = draw 〔 drɔ 〕
   = portray 〔 porˈtre 〕
   = depict 〔 dɪˈpɪkt 〕
   = picture 〔ˈpɪktʃə 〕

2. **party** 〔ˈpɑrtɪ 〕 *v.* 盡情狂歡

   = celebrate 〔ˈsɛləˌbret 〕
   = have fun
   = have a good time
   = enjoy yourself

3. **pleasure** 〔ˈplɛʒə 〕 *n.* 樂趣

   = joy 〔 dʒɔɪ 〕
   = delight 〔 dɪˈlaɪt 〕
   = happiness 〔ˈhæpɪnɪs 〕

   = enjoyment 〔 ɪnˈdʒɔɪmənt 〕
   = amusement 〔 əˈmjuzmənt 〕

4. **present** 〔ˈprɛznt 〕 *adj.* 現在的；
   警覺的；專注的

   ① = current 〔ˈkɝənt 〕
      = contemporary
        〔 kənˈtɛmpəˌrɛrɪ 〕
      = in the moment

   ② = alert 〔ˈəlɝt 〕
      = awake 〔 əˈwek 〕

5. **playful** 〔ˈplefəl 〕 *adj.* 愛玩的

   = cheerful 〔ˈtʃɪrfəl 〕
   = merry 〔ˈmɛrɪ 〕
   = joyous 〔ˈdʒɔɪəs 〕
   = mischievous 〔ˈmɪstʃɪvəs 〕

6. **peaceful** 〔ˈpisfəl 〕 *adj.* 和平的

   = at peace
   = calm 〔 kɑm 〕
   = harmonious 〔 hɑrˈmonɪəs 〕

7. **partner** 〔ˈpɑrtnə 〕 *n.* 夥伴

   = mate 〔 met 〕
   = companion 〔 kəmˈpænjən 〕
   = associate 〔 əˈsoʃɪɪt 〕

8. **pastime** 〔ˈpæsˌtaɪm 〕 *n.* 消遣

   = hobby 〔ˈhɑbɪ 〕
   = recreation 〔ˌrɛkrɪˈeʃən 〕
   = relaxation 〔ˌrilækˈseʃən 〕

   = amusement 〔 əˈmjuzmənt 〕
   = entertainment 〔ˌɛntəˈtenmənt 〕

9. **pet** 〔 pɛt 〕 *n.* 寵物

   = an animal kept for enjoyment
     or companionship

## How to Be Happy

# *17.* P (2)

| 看英文唸出中文 | 一口氣說九句 | 看中文唸出英文 | |
|---|---|---|---|
| **plan**¹<br>〔 plæn 〕 *n. v.* | 是<br>同<br>義<br>字 | Have a *plan*.<br>要有計劃。 | 計劃 |
| **purpose**¹<br>〔 'pɝpəs 〕 *n.* | | *Purpose*.<br>要有目標。 | 目的；目標 |
| **project**²<br>〔 'prɑdʒɛkt 〕 *n.* | | *Project*.<br>要有計劃。 | 計劃 |

P

| | | | |
|---|---|---|---|
| **pleasant**²<br>〔 'plɛznt 〕 *adj.* | 三<br>個<br>形<br>容<br>詞 | Be *pleasant*.<br>要令人愉快。 | 令人愉快的 |
| **practical**³<br>〔 'præktɪkl̩ 〕 *adj.* | | *Practical*.<br>要實際。 | 實際的 |
| **physical**⁴<br>〔 'fɪzɪkl̩ 〕 *adj.* | | Get *physical*.<br>要運動。 | 身體的 |

| | | | |
|---|---|---|---|
| **plant**¹<br>〔 plænt 〕 *v.* | 字<br>首<br>是<br>pla | *Plant* flowers.<br>要種花。 | 種植 |
| **playground**¹<br>〔 'ple‚graʊnd 〕 *n.* | | Hit the *playground*.<br>去遊樂場。 | 遊樂場 |
| **passion**³<br>〔 'pæʃən 〕 *n.* | | Have a strong<br>*passion*.<br>要有強烈的熱情。 | 熱情 |

P

# I. 背景説明：

要快樂，一定要有目標。***Have a plan.*** 可説成：Have a ***plan*** for life. （人生要有計劃。） Make a ***plan*** for the future. （要爲未來做規劃。） ***Purpose.*** 在此指 Have a ***purpose***. （要有目標。） Find a ***purpose*** in life. （要找到人生的目標。） Discover your ***purpose*** of living. （要發現你生活的目標。） purpose 的主要意思是「目的」，在此作「目標」解。***Project.*** 在此指 Have a ***project***. （要有計劃。） 可説成：Start a new ***project***. （要開始一項新的計劃。） Have a number of ***projects*** going at once. （同時要有幾個計劃在進行中。）
【***at once*** 立刻；同時】

***Be pleasant.*** ( = *Be nice.* ) ***Be*** a ***pleasant*** person. （要做一個令人愉快的人。） Have a ***pleasant*** character. （要有令人愉快的個性。） ***Practical.*** 在此指 Be ***practical***. （要實際。） Be a ***practical*** person. （要做一個實際的人。）( = *Be a realistic person.* ) Use ***practical*** methods to solve problems. （要用實際的方法解決問題。） Be ***practical***, not a dreamer. （要實際，不要做夢。） ***Get physical.*** （要運動。）( = *Get some exercise.* ) ***Get*** some ***physical*** exercise. （要做一些運動。） Do some ***physical*** activity. （要做一些身體的活動。）

***Plant flowers.*** 可説成：***Plant*** a garden of ***flowers***. （要把花園種滿花。） ***Plant*** a tree. （要種一棵樹。） ***Hit the playground.*** ( = *Go to the playground.* ) Have fun at the ***playground***. （要在遊樂場好好玩。）【hit〔hɪt〕v. 去】 ***Have a strong passion.*** 可説成：Develop *a* ***strong passion*** for something. （要培養對某事物強烈的熱情。） Be a person with *a* ***strong passion*** for life. （要做一個對人生有強烈熱情的人。）

## II. 英語演講：

### 【一字英語演講】

*Good day:*

*Have a plan.*
*Purpose.*
*Project.*

*Be pleasant.*
*Practical.*
*Get physical.*

*Plant flowers.*
*Hit the playground.*
*Have a strong*
　*passion.*

*These are the*
　*easiest ways to*
　*be happy.*

### 【短篇英語演講】

*Good day:* 大家好：

*Have a plan* for the future. 要為未來做規劃。
Find a *purpose* in life. 要找到人生的目標。
Start a new *project*. 要開始新的計劃。

*Be* a *pleasant* person. 要做一個令人愉快的人。
Use *practical* methods to solve problems.
要用實際的方法解決問題。
*Get* some *physical* exercise.
要做一些運動。

*Plant* a garden of *flowers*. 要把花園種滿花。
*Hit the playground* for fun. 要去遊樂場玩。
*Have a strong passion* for life.
要對人生有強烈的熱情。

*These are the easiest ways to be happy*.
這些就是要快樂最簡單的方法。

## III. 短篇作文：

### The Easiest Ways to Be Happy

　　There are some really easy ways to be happy, and I'm going to tell you about the easiest ones. *First*, have a *plan* for life. Discover your *purpose* of living. Have a number of *projects* going at once. *What's more*, be a *pleasant* person. Use *practical* methods to solve problems. *Get* some *physical* exercise. *Besides*, *plant* a tree. *Hit the playground*. And the easiest way of all, develop a strong *passion* for something and you'll be happy.

### 要快樂最簡單的方法

要快樂,有一些真的很容易的方法,而我要告訴你最簡單的幾個。首先,人生要有計劃。要發現你生活的目標。同時要有幾個計劃在進行中。此外,要做一個令人愉快的人。要用實際的方法解決問題。要做一些運動。還有,要種一棵樹。要去遊樂場。而最簡單的方法,就是要培養對某事物強烈的熱情,那樣你就會快樂。

\* develop〔dɪ'vɛləp〕*v.* 培養

## IV. 填空:

If you make a ___1___ for the future, you're certain to be happy. Likewise, find a ___2___ in life. Start a new and challenging ___3___ .

At the same time, have a ___4___ character. Use ___5___ methods to solve problems. And make sure you get enough ___6___ exercise.

Moreover, ___7___ a garden of flowers. Have fun at the ___8___ . Above all, be a person with a strong ___9___ for life.

如果你為未來做規劃,你一定會快樂。同樣地,要找到人生的目標。要開始一項新的並且有挑戰性的計劃。

同時,要有令人愉快的個性。要用實際的方法解決問題。而且要確定你有充分的運動。

此外,要把花園種滿花。要在遊樂場好好玩。最重要的是,要做一個對人生有強烈熱情的人。

【解答】 1. plan  2. purpose  3. project  4. pleasant  5. practical
6. physical  7. plant  8. playground  9. passion

\* likewise〔'laɪk,waɪz〕*adv.* 同樣地
challenging〔'tʃælɪndʒɪŋ〕*adj.* 有挑戰性的
method〔'mɛθəd〕*n.* 方法    solve〔salv〕*v.* 解決
***have fun*** 玩得愉快    ***above all*** 最重要的是

## V. 詞彙題：

***Directions:*** *Choose the one word that best completes the sentence.*

1. You're never going to accomplish anything without first making a _____.
   (A) patent　(B) pile　(C) plan　(D) photo

2. Once you have a _____, you have a reason for living.
   (A) parade　(B) purpose　(C) pistol　(D) plate

3. Few things are more satisfying than completing a big _____.
   (A) protein　(B) province　(C) proverb　(D) project

4. It takes far less energy to be _____ than it does to be mean.
   (A) pleasant　(B) private　(C) pregnant　(D) potential

5. Have a _____ mindset and you'll be prepared for anything.
   (A) partial　(B) practical　(C) passive　(D) previous

6. There's no substitute for good old _____ activity to get the blood moving.
   (A) physical　(B) pacific　(C) pale　(D) parallel

7. Experience the joy of _____ a garden and watching it grow.
   (A) performing　(B) persisting　(C) planting　(D) plucking

8. Go to your local _____ and have fun with the kids.
   (A) parliament　(B) playground　(C) pharmacy　(D) planet

9. The most successful and happy people have a _____ for what they're doing.
   (A) passport　(B) passage　(C) pastime　(D) passion

【答案】1.（C）　2.（B）　3.（D）　4.（A）　5.（B）　6.（A）
　　　　7.（C）　8.（B）　9.（D）

## VI. 同義字整理：

1. **plan** 〔 plæn 〕 *n. v.* 計劃
   - = idea 〔 aɪˋdɪə 〕
   - = program 〔ˋprogræm 〕
   - = design 〔 dɪˋzaɪn 〕

   - = strategy 〔ˋstrætədʒɪ 〕
   - = scheme 〔 skim 〕

2. **purpose** 〔ˋpɝpəs 〕 *n.* 目的；
   目標
   - = aim 〔 em 〕
   - = goal 〔 gol 〕
   - = objective 〔 əbˋdʒɛktɪv 〕
   - = motivation 〔ˏmotəˋveʃən 〕

3. **project** 〔ˋpradʒɛkt 〕 *n.* 計劃
   - = plan 〔 plæn 〕
   - = program 〔ˋprogræm 〕
   - = scheme 〔 skim 〕
   - = undertaking 〔ˏʌndɚˋtekɪŋ 〕

4. **pleasant** 〔ˋplɛznt 〕 *adj.* 令人愉
   快的
   - = lovely 〔ˋlʌvlɪ 〕
   - = friendly 〔ˋfrɛndlɪ 〕
   - = pleasing 〔ˋplizɪŋ 〕
   - = agreeable 〔 əˋgriəbl 〕

5. **practical** 〔ˋpræktɪkl 〕 *adj.*
   實際的

   - = realistic 〔ˏriəˋlɪstɪk 〕
   - = sensible 〔ˋsɛnsəbl 〕
   - = pragmatic 〔 prægˋmætɪk 〕
   - = down-to-earth 〔ˏdauntəˋɝθ 〕

6. **physical** 〔ˋfɪzɪkl 〕 *adj.* 身體的
   - = bodily 〔ˋbadɪlɪ 〕
   - = fleshly 〔ˋflɛʃlɪ 〕
   - = corporal 〔ˋkɔrpərəl 〕

7. **plant** 〔 plænt 〕 *v.* 種植
   - = sow 〔 so 〕
   - = scatter 〔ˋskætɚ 〕
   - = set out
   - = put in the ground

8. **playground** 〔ˋpleˏgraund 〕 *n.*
   遊樂場
   - = play park
   - = play area
   - = recreation area

9. **passion** 〔ˋpæʃən 〕 *n.* 熱情
   - = love 〔 lʌv 〕
   - = zeal 〔 zil 〕
   - = desire 〔 dɪˋzaɪr 〕

   - = emotion 〔 ɪˋmoʃən 〕
   - = enthusiasm 〔 ɪnˋθjuzɪˏæzəm 〕

**How to Be Happy**

# *18.* R

| 看英文唸出中文 | 一口氣說九句 | 看中文唸出英文 |
|---|---|---|

**rest**[1]
〔rɛst〕 *v. n.*

**risk**[3]
〔rɪsk〕 *v.*

**relaxed**[3]
〔rɪ'lækst〕 *adj.*

兩個動詞

*Rest.*
要休息。　　　　　休息

*Risk.*
要冒險。　　　　　冒…的危險

Be *relaxed.*
要放輕鬆。　　　　放鬆的

---

**realistic**[4]
〔͵riə'lɪstɪk〕 *adj.*

**rational**[6]
〔'ræʃənḷ〕 *adj.*

**reasonable**[3]
〔'riznəbḷ〕 *adj.*

三個形容詞

*Realistic.*
要實際。　　　　　實際的

*Rational.*
要理性。　　　　　理性的

Truly *reasonable.*
要非常理智。　　　合理的；理智的

---

**recreation**[4]
〔͵rɛkrɪ'eʃən〕 *n.*

**refreshment**[6]
〔rɪ'frɛʃmənt〕 *n.*

**romance**[4]
〔ro'mæns〕 *n.*

三個名詞

Seek *recreation.*
要找樂子。　　　　娛樂

*Refreshment.*
要恢復精神。　　　恢復精神

*Romance.*
要談戀愛。　　　　羅曼史

# I. 背景說明：

*Rest*. ( 要休息。) ( = *Relax*. ) 可說成：Take time to *rest*. ( 要找時間休息。) *Rest* often. ( 要常休息。) rest 也可當名詞，如 Get some *rest*. ( 要休息一下。) Get plenty of *rest*. ( 要多休息。) *Risk*. ( 要冒險。) ( = *Take a chance*. ) 可說成：*Risk* it all. ( 要孤注一擲。) ( = *Take a big chance*. ) Be willing to *risk* something. ( 要願意冒險。) *Be relaxed*. ( 要放鬆。) *Be relaxed* and easygoing. ( 要輕鬆悠哉。) *Be* a *relaxed* person. ( 要做一個輕輕鬆鬆的人。)

*Realistic*. 在此指 Be *realistic*. ( 要實際。) ( = *Be a realistic person*. ) Be *realistic* about life. ( 對人生要實際；不要對人生有太大的期望。) ( = *Don't have great expectations of life*. ) *Rational*. 在此指 Be *rational*. ( 要理性。) ( = *Be a rational person*. ) Have a *rational* mind. ( 想法要理性。) *Truly reasonable*. 可說成：Be a *truly reasonable* person. ( 要做一個非常理智的人。) Be genuinely *reasonable* and easy to work with. ( 要非常理智，並且容易和人合作。) truly 和 genuinely 的字面意思是「眞正地」，在此作「非常地」解。

*Seek recreation*. 可說成：*Seek recreation* outdoors. ( 要到戶外找樂子。) ( = *Seek recreation in the outdoors*. ) Be enthusiastic about *recreation*. ( 要熱中於娛樂。) *Refreshment*. 在此指 Seek *refreshment*. ( 要恢復精神。) Take time for some *refreshment*. ( 要找時間恢復精神。) ( = *Make time for some refreshment*. ) 複數形 refreshments 指「點心」( = *snacks* )，如：Buy some *refreshments* at the market. ( 要在市場買一些點心。) *Romance*. 在此指 Seek *romance*. ( 要談戀愛。) Start a new *romance*. ( 要談一次新的戀愛。) ( = *Get involved in a new romance*. ) romance 的意思有：「羅曼史；韻事；言情作品；文藝愛情片；浪漫傳奇」。

## II. 英語演講：

### 【一字英語演講】

*Greetings*, *everybody*:

*Rest.*
*Risk.*
*Be relaxed.*

*Realistic.*
*Rational.*
*Truly reasonable.*

*Seek recreation.*
*Refreshment.*
*Romance.*

*These are habits of*
*happy people.*

### 【短篇英語演講】

*Greetings*, *everybody:* 大家好：

*Rest* often.  要常休息。
Be willing to *risk* something.  要願意冒險。
*Be relaxed* and easygoing.  要輕鬆悠哉。

Be *realistic* about life.  對人生要實際。
Be a *rational* person.  要理性。
Be *truly reasonable* and easy to work with.
要非常理性，並且容易和人合作。

*Seek recreation* in the outdoors.
要到戶外找樂子。
Take time for some *refreshment*.
要找時間恢復精神。
Get involved in a new *romance*.
要談一次新的戀愛。

*These are habits of happy people*.
這些都是快樂的人的習慣。

R

## III. 短篇作文：

### Habits of Happy People

Happy people are just like you and me.  They have habits and routines.  Maybe you could borrow a few tips from them. *To start with*, get plenty of *rest*.  Be willing to *risk* something. *Yet*, *be* a *relaxed* person. *Additionally*, be a *realistic* person.  Have a *rational* mind.  Be a *truly reasonable* person. *Most importantly*, be enthusiastic about *recreation*.  Make time for some *refreshment*. Start a new *romance*.  Adopt these habits and be a happy person.

### 快樂的人的習慣

快樂的人就像你我一樣。他們有習慣和例行公事。也許你可以向他們借用一些祕訣。首先,要多休息。要願意冒險。但是,要做一個輕輕鬆鬆的人。此外,要實際。想法要理性。要做一個非常理性的人。最重要的是,要熱中於娛樂。要找時間恢復精神。要談一次新的戀愛。有了這些習慣,就能成為快樂的人。

> \* routine〔ru'tin〕*n.* 例行公事
> ***make time*** 騰出時間　　adopt〔ə'dɑpt〕*v.* 採用

## IV. 填空:

Happy people generally ___1___ frequently.  On the other hand, they're willing to ___2___ failure in order to succeed.  They're also ___3___ and easygoing.

What's more, happy people are ___4___ about life.  They are deeply ___5___ people.  They're genuinely ___6___ and easy to work with.

Most of all, happy people seek ___7___ in the outdoors.  They take time for some ___8___ .  And they're eager to get involved in a new ___9___ .

快樂的人通常會常休息。另一方面,為了要成功,他們會願意冒失敗的風險。他們也很輕鬆悠哉。

此外,快樂的人對人生很實際。他們是非常理性的人。他們非常理性,並且容易和人合作。

最重要的是,快樂的人會去戶外找樂子。他們會找時間恢復精神。而且他們會很渴望談一次新的戀愛。

【解答】 1. rest  2. risk  3. relaxed  4. realistic  5. rational
　　　　 6. reasonable  7. recreation  8. refreshment  9. romance
> \* easygoing〔'izɪˏgoɪŋ〕*adj.* 悠哉的;隨遇而安的
> ***get involved in*** 捲入;參與;忙於

## V. 詞彙題：

**Directions:** *Choose the one word that best completes the sentence.*

1. Studies show that the majority of people don't get enough _____ .

   (A) reef　(B) rest　(C) rein　(D) rent

2. Only _____ what you can afford to lose.
   (A) rub　(B) rust　(C) rise　(D) risk

3. You'll perform better when you're calm and _____.
   (A) relaxed　(B) recycled　(C) recorded　(D) recruited

4. It's wise to have _____ expectations of life.
   (A) ritual　(B) royal　(C) realistic　(D) rotten

5. Use your best judgment to make _____ decisions.
   (A) racial　(B) rational　(C) rash　(D) reckless

6. The best way is always the most _____ way.
   (A) random　(B) respective　(C) reasonable　(D) rare

7. Everybody needs more _____ in life.
   (A) repetition　(B) rejection　(C) resignation　(D) recreation

8. It's fun to buy _____ at the night market.
   (A) refreshments　(B) resentment　(C) replacement
   (D) retirement

9. There's nothing like a new _____ to make things interesting.
   (A) reliance　(B) reference　(C) romance　(D) resemblance

【答案】1.（B）　2.（D）　3.（A）　4.（C）　5.（B）　6.（C）
　　　　7.（D）　8.（A）　9.（C）

## VI. 同義字整理：

1. **rest**〔rɛst〕*v. n.* 休息

> = break〔brek〕
> = time off
> = breather〔'briðɚ〕
> = relaxation〔ˌrilæks'eʃən〕

**R**

2. **risk**〔rɪsk〕*v.* 冒…的危險

> = chance〔tʃæns〕
> = venture〔'vɛntʃɚ〕
> = gamble〔'gæmbļ〕

3. **relaxed**〔rɪ'lækst〕*adj.* 放鬆的

> = easygoing〔'izɪˌgoɪŋ〕
> = laid-back〔'ledˌbæk〕
> = mellow〔'mɛlo〕
> = leisurely〔'liʒɚlɪ〕

4. **realistic**〔ˌriə'lɪstɪk〕*adj.* 實際的

> = practical〔'præktɪkļ〕
> = sensible〔'sɛnsəbļ〕
> = rational〔'ræʃənļ〕

> = reasonable〔'riznəbļ〕
> = down-to-earth
>   〔ˌdaʊntə'ɝθ〕

5. **rational**〔'ræʃənļ〕*adj.* 理性的

> = sensible〔'sɛnsəbļ〕
> = reasonable〔'riznəbļ〕
> = realistic〔ˌriə'lɪstɪk〕
> = logical〔'lɑdʒɪkļ〕

6. **reasonable**〔'riznəbļ〕*adj.* 合理的；理智的

> = rational〔'ræʃənļ〕
> = sensible〔'sɛnsəbļ〕
> = logical〔'lɑdʒɪkļ〕

7. **recreation**〔ˌrɛkrɪ'eʃən〕*n.* 娛樂

> = relaxation〔ˌrilæks'eʃən〕
> = amusement〔ə'mjuzmənt〕
> = entertainment〔ˌɛntɚ'tenmənt〕

8. **refreshment**〔rɪ'frɛʃmənt〕*n.* 恢復精神；(*pl.*) 點心

① > = revival〔rɪ'vaɪvļ〕
> = renewal〔ri'njuəl〕
> = freshening〔'frɛʃənɪŋ〕

② > = food and drinks
> = snacks〔snæks〕

9. **romance**〔ro'mæns〕*n.* 羅曼史

> = affair〔ə'fɛr〕
> = love affair
> = relationship〔rɪ'leʃənˌʃɪp〕

**How to Be Happy**

# *19.* S

| 看英文唸出中文 | 一 口 氣 說 九 句 | 看中文唸出英文 |
|---|---|---|

**shower**[2]
〔'ʃauɚ 〕 *v.*

**shop**[1]
〔 ʃɑp 〕 *v.*

**sing**[1]
〔 sɪŋ 〕 *v.*

字首是 Sho

*Shower*.
要淋浴。

*Shop*.
要逛街購物。

*Sing*.
要唱歌。

淋浴

購物

唱歌

---

**simplify**[6]
〔'sɪmplə,faɪ 〕 *v.*

**simply**[2]
〔'sɪmplɪ 〕 *adv.*

**serenity**[6]
〔 sə'rɛnətɪ 〕 *n.*

詞類變化

字首是 si

*Simplify*.
要簡化。

Live *simply*.
要簡單過生活。

Seek *serenity*.
要尋求寧靜。

簡化

簡單地

寧靜

---

**stroll**[5]
〔 strol 〕 *n. v.*

**sun**[1]
〔 sʌn 〕 *n.*

**spin**[3]
〔 spɪn 〕 *n.*

Take a *stroll*.
要去散步。

Get some *sun*.
要去曬曬太陽。

Go for a *spin*.
要去兜風。

字尾是 n

散步

太陽

兜風

## I. 背景說明：

  *Shower*. 可說成：*Shower* daily. ( 要每天淋浴。) *Shower* and you'll be refreshed. ( 去淋浴你就會恢復精神。) *Showering* makes you happy. ( 淋浴會使你快樂。) shower 也可當名詞，如：Take a long hot *shower*. ( 要好好地用熱水淋浴。) *Shop*. 可說成：Go *shopping*. ( 要去逛街購物。) *Shop* for some gifts. ( 要去買一些禮物。)( = *Go shopping for some gifts.* = *Buy some gifts.* ) *Sing*. 可說成：*Sing* out loud. ( 要唱出聲音來。)( = *Sing aloud.* ) *Sing* loudly. ( 要大聲唱歌。)( = *Sing at a loud volume.* ) *Sing* a song. ( 要唱一首歌。)

  *Simplify*. 可說成：*Simplify* your life. ( 要簡化你的生活。) *Simplify* your daily routine. ( 要簡化你每天的例行事務。) *Live simply*. 可說成：*Live simply* and modestly. ( 要過得簡單樸實。) *Live simply* and peacefully. ( 要過得簡單又平靜。) *Seek serenity*. 可說成：*Seek serenity* and peace. ( 要找到寧靜。) *Seek serenity* in nature. ( 要在大自然中找到寧靜。)( = *Seek peace outdoors.* )

  *Take a stroll*. ( 要去散步。)( = *Take a walk.* ) *Take a stroll* in the park. ( 要在公園裡散步。) *Take a stroll* along the riverside. ( 要沿著河邊散步。) *Get some sun*. ( = *Get some sunshine.* ) 可說成：*Get* outdoors for *some sun*. ( 要到戶外曬曬太陽。) sun 可作「太陽」或「陽光」解。 *Go for a spin*. ( = *Go for a ride.* = *Take a ride.* ) *Go for a spin* on your bicycle. ( 要騎腳踏車去兜風。) *Go for a spin* around the block. ( 要在街區兜風。) *Go for a spin* in your car. ( 要開車去兜風。) spin 的主要意思是動詞「旋轉」，在此當名詞，作「兜風」解。

## II. 英語演講：

### 【一字英語演講】

*Friends and associates:*

*Shower.*
*Shop.*
*Sing.*

*Simplify.*
*Live simply.*
*Seek serenity.*

*Take a stroll.*
*Get some sun.*
*Go for a spin.*

*Try these fun ways to be happy.*

### 【短篇英語演講】

*Friends and associates:* 各位朋友和同事：

*Showering* makes you happy. 淋浴會使你快樂。
Go *shopping* for some gifts. 要去買一些禮物。
*Sing* a song. 要唱一首歌。

*Simplify* your daily routine.
要簡化你每天的例行事務。
*Live simply* and modestly. 要過得簡單樸實。
*Seek serenity* and peace. 要找到寧靜。

*Take a stroll* along the riverside.
要沿著河邊散步。
*Get* outdoors for *some sun*. 要到戶外曬曬太陽。
*Go for a spin* on your bicycle.
要騎腳踏車去兜風。

*Try these fun ways to be happy*.
試試這些能使人快樂的有趣方法。

## III. 短篇作文：

### Fun Ways to Be Happy

Happiness and fun go together like bread and butter. Check out these fun ways to be happy. *First of all*, take a long hot *shower*. *Shop* for some gifts. *Sing* loudly. *Besides*, *simplify* everything in your life. *Live simply* and modestly. *Seek serenity* in nature. *Additionally*, *take a stroll* in the park. *Get some sun*. And perhaps the most fun way to be happy is: *Go for a spin* around the block.

### 能使人快樂的有趣方法

　　快樂和有趣就像麵包和奶油一樣，密切相關。看看這些能使人快樂的有趣方法。首先，要好好地用熱水淋浴。要去買一些禮物。要大聲唱歌。此外，要簡化你生活中的一切。要過得簡單樸實。要在大自然中找到寧靜。而且，要在公園裡散步。要去曬曬太陽。而且或許能快樂的最有趣的方法就是：去街區兜風。

* ***go together*** 密切相關　　fun〔 fʌn 〕*adj.* 有趣的
  modestly〔ˋmɑdɪstlɪ〕*adv.* 樸實地
  block〔 blɑk 〕*n.* 街區

## IV. 填空：

　　If you're having a bad day, ＿＿1＿＿ will make you happy. Go ＿＿2＿＿ for some gifts.  On the other hand, ＿＿3＿＿ a song.

　　Meanwhile, ＿＿4＿＿ your daily routine.  Live ＿＿5＿＿ and modestly.  Seek ＿＿6＿＿ and peace in meditation exercises.

　　What's more, take a ＿＿7＿＿ along the riverside.  Get outdoors for some ＿＿8＿＿.  Go for a ＿＿9＿＿ on your bicycle.

　　如果你今天過得不愉快，淋浴會使你快樂。去逛街買一些禮物。另一方面，要唱一首歌。

　　同時，要簡化你每天的例行事務。要過得簡單樸實。在練習打坐時找到平靜。

　　此外，要沿著河邊散步。要到戶外曬曬太陽。要騎腳踏車去兜風。

【解答】1. showering　2. shopping　3. sing　4. simplify
　　　　5. simply　6. serenity　7. stroll　8. sun　9. spin
* ***have a bad day*** 今天過得不愉快
  routine〔 ruˋtin 〕*n.* 例行公事　　peace〔 pis 〕*n.* 平靜；寧靜
  meditation〔ˌmɛdəˋteʃən〕*n.* 沈思；打坐；冥想

## V. 詞彙題：

***Directions:*** *Choose the one word that best completes the sentence.*

1. Japanese people usually _____ in the evening to "wash off" the day.
   (A) shine　(B) shout　(C) shriek　(D) shower

2. It's fun to _____ for souvenirs at the night market, isn't it?
   (A) share　(B) shop　(C) settle　(D) shave

3. Me and my friends like to get together and _____ karaoke.
   (A) sign　(B) sigh　(C) sing　(D) sink

4. Life is much easier when you _____ your schedule.
   (A) simplify　(B) scrub　(C) shrug　(D) seduce

5. The most content people are happy to live _____ and modestly.
   (A) superficially　(B) suddenly　(C) statistically　(D) simply

6. Many people find peace and _____ in nature.
   (A) serenity　(B) sincerity　(C) specialty　(D) similarity

7. After dinner, let's go for a _____ along the riverside.
   (A) scroll　(B) stroll　(C) shell　(D) skill

8. Following a week of rain, it was nice to see the _____ for a change.
   (A) suit　(B) stove　(C) sun　(D) steak

9. If you've nothing to do, go for a _____ on your motorcycle.
   (A) spine　(B) spin　(C) spice　(D) spider

【答案】1.(D)　2.(B)　3.(C)　4.(A)　5.(D)　6.(A)
　　　　7.(B)　8.(C)　9.(B)

## VI. 同義字整理：

1. **shower** 〔'ʃauɚ 〕 *v. n.* 淋浴
   - = take a shower
   - = wash up
   - = bathe 〔 beð 〕

2. **shop** 〔 ʃɑp 〕 *v.* 購物
   - = go shopping
   - = do the shopping
   - = go to the shops
   - = buy things

3. **sing** 〔 sɪŋ 〕 *v.* 唱歌
   - = croon 〔 krun 〕
   - = carol 〔'kærəl 〕
   - = chant 〔 tʃænt 〕
   - = vocalize 〔'vokl̩,aɪz 〕

4. **simplify** 〔'sɪmplə,faɪ 〕 *v.* 簡化
   - = make simpler
   - = facilitate 〔 fə'sɪlə,tet 〕
   - = streamline 〔'strim,laɪn 〕
   - = disentangle 〔,dɪsɪn'tæŋgl̩ 〕
   - = reduce to essentials

5. **simply** 〔'sɪmplɪ 〕 *adv.* 簡單地
   - = plainly 〔'plenlɪ 〕
   - = naturally 〔'nætʃərəlɪ 〕
   - = modestly 〔'mɑdɪstlɪ 〕

6. **serenity** 〔 sə'rɛnətɪ 〕 *n.* 寧靜
   - = calm 〔 kɑm 〕
   - = peace 〔 pis 〕
   - = tranquility 〔 træŋ'kwɪlətɪ 〕
   - = quietness 〔'kwaɪətnɪs 〕

7. **stroll** 〔 strol 〕 *n. v.* 散步
   - = walk 〔 wɔk 〕
   - = ramble 〔'ræmbl̩ 〕
   - = airing 〔'ɛrɪŋ 〕
   - = promenade 〔,prɑmə'ned 〕

8. **sun** 〔 sʌn 〕 *n.* 太陽
   - = sunshine 〔'sʌn,ʃaɪn 〕
   - = sunlight 〔'sʌn,laɪt 〕
   - = daylight 〔'de,laɪt 〕

9. **spin** 〔 spɪn 〕 *n.* 兜風
   - = drive 〔 draɪv 〕
   - = ride 〔 raɪd 〕
   - = turn 〔 tɜn 〕
   - = joy ride

**S**

# How to Be Happy

## *20.* T

| 看英文唸出中文 | 一口氣說九句 | 看中文唸出英文 |
|---|---|---|
| **talk**[1]<br>〔 tɔk 〕*v.* | 三個動詞 {<br>*Talk*.<br>要說話。<br>*Touch* someone.<br>要使人感動。<br>*Treat* somebody.<br>要請客。 | 說話 <br><br>接觸；<br>使感動<br><br>對待；招待 |
| **touch**[1]<br>〔 tʌtʃ 〕*v. n.* | | |
| **treat**[5,2]<br>〔 trit 〕*v.* | | |
| **tour**[2]<br>〔 tʊr 〕*n.* | 三個名詞 {<br>Take a *tour*.<br>要去旅遊。<br>*Trip*.<br>要去旅行。<br>*Trek*.<br>要去徒步旅行。 意思相近 | 旅遊 <br><br>旅行<br><br><br>徒步旅行 |
| **trip**[1]<br>〔 trɪp 〕*n. v.* | | |
| **trek**[6]<br>〔 trɛk 〕*n.* | | |
| **treasure**[2]<br>〔ˈtrɛʒɚ 〕*n.* | 三個名詞 {<br>Seek *treasure*.<br>要尋寶。<br>*Triumph*.<br>要追求勝利。<br>A *thrill*.<br>要尋找令人興奮的事。 字首是 tr | 寶藏 <br><br>勝利<br><br><br>令人興奮的事 |
| **triumph**[4]<br>〔ˈtraɪəmf 〕*n.* | | |
| **thrill**[5]<br>〔 θrɪl 〕*n.* | | |

T

## I. 背景説明：

*Talk*. 可説成：*Talk* to people.（要和人説話。）*Talk* to your friends.（要和你的朋友説話。）*Talking* to people makes you happy.（和人説話會使你快樂。）*Touch someone*.（= *Make someone feel good*.）*Touch someone*'s heart.（要感動人心。）touch 也可當名詞，Get in *touch* with an old friend.（要和老朋友聯絡。）其實，「聯絡」就會「使」人「感動」。 touch 的意思有：「觸摸；接觸；使感動。」*Treat somebody*.（= *Treat someone*.）可説成：*Treat* people to some ice cream.（要請人吃一些冰淇淋。）*Treat* your friends to a night out.（要招待你的朋友晚上出去玩。）（= *Treat your friends to an evening of activity*.）

*Take a tour*. 可説成：*Take a tour* of a foreign country.（要出國旅遊。）*Take a tour* of a museum.（要去博物館參觀。）tour 的意思有：「旅遊；觀光；參觀」。*Trip*. 在此指 Take a *trip*.（要去旅行。）可説成：Take a *trip* out of town.（要到外地去旅行。）（= *Travel somewhere*.）Take a *trip* to a faraway land.（要到遙遠的地方旅行。）（= *Take a trip to a place that is far away*.）*Trek*. 在此指 Take a *trek*.（要去徒步旅行。）Take a *trek* in a foreign country.（要到國外徒步旅行。）Take a *trek* in the mountains.（要到山上徒步旅行。）trek 是指「漫長、艱苦的徒步旅行」（*a walk that seems long and difficult*）。

*Seek treasure*.（= *Go looking for good things*.）Seek *treasure* in friendship.（要珍惜你的朋友。）（= *Cherish your friends*. = *Find value in having friends*.）朋友即是你的寶藏，要珍惜他們，朋友

會給你帶來快樂。Look for *treasure* in hidden places. ( 要在隱密的地方尋寶。) ( = *Look for value where you can't see it.* ) *Triumph*. 在此指 Seek *triumph*. ( 要追求勝利。) Seek a *triumph* of good over evil. ( 要讓正義戰勝邪惡。) Celebrate a *triumph*. ( 要慶祝⋯⋯「當動詞，作「獲勝」解。Seek to *triumph* over evil. ( 要努力⋯⋯戰勝邪惡。) *A thrill*. 在此指 Seek *a thrill*. 「要尋找令人興奮的⋯⋯。」( = *Seek some excitement.* ) Get *a thrill* from hard work. ⋯⋯要因為努力工作而感到興奮。) Enjoy the *thrill* of an amuse⋯⋯nt park. ( 要享受遊樂園的刺激。) 【*amusement park* 遊樂園 ( 如⋯⋯士尼樂園等 )】 thrill 的意思有：「興奮；激動；緊張；使人興奮的事⋯⋯令人喜悅的事物」。thrill 也可當動詞，作「使興奮」解 ( = *exc*⋯⋯。I'm *thrilled* to be here. ( 我今天非常高興來到這裡。)

*Grea⋯⋯ see so many smil⋯⋯faces:*

Talk.
Touch some⋯⋯
Treat somebo⋯⋯

Take a tour.
Trip.
Trek.

Seek treasure.
Triumph.
A thrill.

*Do this, and happiness is guaranteed.*

## II. 短篇英語演講：

*Great to see so many smiling faces:*
很高興看到這麼多張笑臉：

*Talk* to your friends.　要和你的朋友說話。
*Touch someone*'s heart　要感動人心。
*Treat* people to some ice cream.　要請人吃一些冰淇淋。

*Take a tour* of a museum.　要去參觀博物館。
Take a *trip* out of town.　要到外地去旅行。
Take a *trek* in a foreign country.　要到國外去徒步旅行。

*Seek treasure* in friendship.　要珍惜你的朋友。
Seek a *triumph* of good over evil.　要讓正義戰勝邪惡。
Enjoy the *thrill* of an amusement park.　要享受遊樂園的刺激。

*Do this*, *and happiness is guaranteed*.　這麼做保證你會快樂。

## III. 短篇作文：

### Guaranteed Happiness

Life doesn't offer many guarantees. *However*, there are some things that are certain to bring you happiness. *For starters*, *talking* to people makes you happy. Get in *touch* with an old friend. *Treat* your friends to a night out. *In a similar way*, *take a tour* of a foreign country. Take a *trip* to a faraway land. Take a *trek* in the mountains. *What's more*, look for *treasure* in hidden places. Celebrate a *triumph*. Get *a thrill* from hard work and happiness is guaranteed.

### 保證會快樂

　　人生不能保證很多事。然而，有些事一定會帶給你快樂。首先，和人說話會使你快樂。要和老朋友聯絡。要招待你的朋友晚上出去玩。同樣地，要出國旅遊。要到遙遠的地方旅行。要到山上徒步旅行。此外，要在隱密的地方尋寶。要慶祝勝利。要因爲努力工作而感到興奮，那樣就保證一定會快樂。

> \* guarantee〔͵gærən'ti〕*n. v.* 保證　　***for starters*** 首先
> hidden〔'hɪdṇ〕*adj.* 隱藏的；祕密的　　***in a similar way*** 同樣地
> faraway〔'farə'we〕*adj.* 遙遠的

## IV. 填空：

　　If you really want happiness, ___1___ to your friends. Likewise, ___2___ someone's heart. ___3___ people to some ice cream.

　　Meanwhile, take a ___4___ of a museum. Take a ___5___ out of town. Take a ___6___ to a foreign country you've always wanted to visit.

　　More importantly, seek ___7___ in friendship. Seek a ___8___ of good over evil. Enjoy the ___9___ of an amusement park and happiness is guaranteed.

　　如果你眞的想要快樂，就要和你的朋友說話。同樣地，要感動人心。要請人吃一些冰淇淋。

　　同時，要去博物館參觀。要到外地去旅行。要到你一直很想去的外國徒步旅行。

　　更重要的是，要珍惜你的朋友。要讓正義戰勝邪惡。要享受遊樂園的刺激，這樣就保證一定能快樂。

【解答】1. talk　2. touch　3. Treat　4. tour　5. trip　6. trek
　　　　7. treasure　8. triumph　9. thrill

> \* ***out of town*** 出城；到外地　　good〔gud〕*n.* 善
> evil〔'ivḷ〕*n.* 邪惡　　***amusement park*** 遊樂園

## V. 詞彙題：

***Directions:*** *Choose the one word that best completes the sentence.*

1. It's important to _____ about your feelings and get them out in the open.
   (A) tease   (B) tap   (C) taunt   (D) talk

2. A kind gesture is guaranteed to _____ a stranger's heart.
   (A) toss   (B) tolerate   (C) tangle   (D) touch

3. Generous people get happiness from _____ their friends to dinner.
   (A) trimming   (B) treating   (C) triggering   (D) treading

4. Join a _____ group and travel to an exotic location.
   (A) tour   (B) tower   (C) tough   (D) toxic

5. Plan a weekend _____ to a cottage at the seashore with your partner.
   (A) tray   (B) trade   (C) trip   (D) trap

6. Take a _____ through the Grand Canyon or some other natural wonder.
   (A) track   (B) trek   (C) trail   (D) trait

7. There is _____ to be found if you know where to look for it.
   (A) temperature   (B) torture   (C) treasure   (D) texture

8. Earning a college degree is a major _____ in life.
   (A) triumph   (B) telegraph   (C) torch   (D) trench

9. Do something crazy just for the _____ of it.
   (A) toil   (B) tool   (C) toll   (D) thrill

【答案】1.（D）　2.（D）　3.（B）　4.（A）　5.（C）　6.（B）
　　　　7.（C）　8.（A）　9.（D）

## VI. 同義字整理：

1. **talk**〔tɔk〕 *v.* 說話
   - = speak〔spik〕
   - = chat〔tʃæt〕
   - = converse〔kən'vɜs〕
   - = communicate〔kə'mjunə‚ket〕

2. **touch**〔tʌtʃ〕 *v. n.* 接觸；使感動
   - = affect〔ə'fɛkt〕
   - = influence〔'ɪnfluəns〕
   - = inspire〔ɪn'spaɪr〕

   - = impress〔ɪm'prɛs〕
   - = have an effect on
   - = make an impression on

3. **treat**〔trit〕 *v.* 對待；招待
   - = provide〔prə'vaɪd〕
   - = give〔gɪv〕
   - = buy〔baɪ〕
   - = pay for

4. **tour**〔tur〕 *n.* 旅遊
   - = trip〔trɪp〕
   - = journey〔'dʒɜnɪ〕
   - = outing〔'autɪŋ〕

   - = excursion〔ɪk'skɜʒən〕
   - = expedition〔‚ɛkspɪ'dɪʃən〕

5. **trip**〔trɪp〕 *n. v.* 旅行
   - = tour〔tur〕
   - = journey〔'dʒɜnɪ〕
   - = travel〔'trævl̩〕

   - = outing〔'autɪŋ〕
   - = excursion〔ɪk'skɜʒən〕

6. **trek**〔trɛk〕 *n.* 徒步旅行
   - = hike〔haɪk〕
   - = expedition〔‚ɛkspɪ'dɪʃən〕
   - = safari〔sə'farɪ〕
   - = odyssey〔'adəsɪ〕

7. **treasure**〔'trɛʒɚ〕 *n.* 寶藏
   - = riches〔'rɪtʃɪz〕
   - = fortune〔'fɔrtʃən〕
   - = wealth〔wɛlθ〕

8. **triumph**〔'traɪəmf〕 *n.* 勝利
   - = success〔sək'sɛs〕
   - = victory〔'vɪktərɪ〕
   - = accomplishment〔ə'kamplɪʃmənt〕
   - = achievement〔ə'tʃivmənt〕

9. **thrill**〔θrɪl〕 *n.* 令人興奮的事
   - = kick〔kɪk〕
   - = sensation〔sɛn'seʃən〕
   - = stimulation〔‚stɪmjə'leʃən〕
   - = flush of excitement

**T**

## How to Be Happy

# *21.* U

| 看英文唸出中文 | 一口氣說九句 | 看中文唸出英文 |
|---|---|---|

**update** [5]
〔 ʌpˈdet 〕 *v.*

字首是 Up
> *Update.*
> 要跟得上時代。

更新

**upgrade** [6]
〔ˈʌpˈgred 〕 *v.*

> *Upgrade.*
> 要升級。

使升級

**undertake** [6]
〔ˌʌndɚˈtek 〕 *v.*

> *Undertake* a challenge.
> 要承擔一項挑戰。

承擔；從事

---

**useful** [1]
〔ˈjusfəl 〕 *adj.*

三個形容詞
> Be *useful.*
> 要做個有用的人。

有用的

**upright** [5]
〔ˈʌpˌraɪt 〕 *adj.*

> *Upright.*
> 要正直。

正直的

**unique** [4]
〔 juˈnik 〕 *adj.*

> *Unique.*
> 要獨一無二。

獨特的

---

**understanding** [1]
〔ˌʌndɚˈstændɪŋ 〕 *adj.*

字首是 un
> *Understanding.*
> 要體諒。

能諒解的

**uncomplaining** [2]
〔ˌʌnkəmˈplenɪŋ 〕 *adj.*

> *Uncomplaining.*
> 不抱怨。

不抱怨的

**unity** [3]
〔ˈjunətɪ 〕 *n.*

> Seek *unity.*
> 要團結。

統一；(團結) 一致

## I. 背景說明：

*Update.* ( = *Bring up to date.* = *Renew.* ) ***Update*** your wardrobe. ( 你的服裝要跟得上時代。)【wardrobe (ˈwɔrd‚rob ) *n.* 衣櫥；服裝】( = *Update your collection of clothes.* ) ***Update*** your fashion style. ( 你服裝的風格要更新。) 如以前男士襯衫都會紮進褲子裡，現在的趨勢是襯衫放在外面。( The old style was to tuck your shirt into the waistband of your pants. The new style is to leave the shirt untucked. )

*Update* your style.

old style

new style

正式場合，還是需要把襯衫紮進去。

*Update* your hairstyle. ( 你的髮型要跟得上時代。)

old style

new style

*Upgrade.* (= *Improve.*) ***Upgrade*** your apartment. ( 要改善你的公寓。) (= *Improve your apartment.*) ***Upgrade*** your living conditions. ( 要改善你的生活環境。) 在機場辦理登機手續時,可問櫃台:How much would it cost to ***upgrade*** from economy to business class? ( 從經濟艙升等到商務艙,要多少錢?)

***Undertake a challenge.*** 在這裡是指「要承擔一項挑戰。」 (= *Accept a challenge.*) undertake 的意思有:「企圖;從事;著手;開始進行;承擔」。***Undertake*** a difficult task. ( 要從事一項困難的任務。) ***Undertake*** a project. ( 要開始做一項計劃。)

*Be useful.* ( = *Be a useful person.* ) Learn *useful* skills. ( 要學習有用的技術。) *Upright.* 在此指 Be *upright.* ( 要正直。) ( = *Be an upright person.* ) Be honest and *upright.* ( 要非常正直。) *Unique.* 在此指 Be *unique.* ( 要獨一無二。) Be a *unique* individual. ( 要做一個獨特的人。) Have a *unique* outlook on life. ( 要有獨特的人生觀。)

*Understanding.* 在此指 Be *understanding.* ( 要體諒。) ( = *Be compassionate.* 要有同情心。) Be an *understanding* person. ( 要做一個能體諒的人。) Be *understanding* and reasonable. ( 要通情達理。) *Uncomplaining.* 在此指 Be *uncomplaining.* ( 不抱怨。) ( = *Be an uncomplaining person.* ) Be indifferent and *uncomplaining.* ( 要不在乎、不抱怨。) *Seek unity.* ( = *Seek togetherness.* ) *Seek unity* among your friends. ( 要促進朋友之間的團結，和睦相處。) ( = *Try to help everybody get along.* = *Promote harmony in the group.* ) *Seek unity* within the community. ( 在社區中要尋求團結一致。) ( = *Promote harmony within the neighborhood.* )

## II. 英語演講：

### 【一字英語演講】

*Boys*, *girls*, *teachers*, *and parents:*

*Update.*
*Upgrade.*
*Undertake a challenge.*

*Be useful.*
*Upright.*
*Unique.*

*Understanding.*
*Uncomplaining.*
*Seek unity.*

*These are keys to happiness.*

### 【短篇英語演講】

*Boys*, *girls*, *teachers*, *and parents:*
各位男孩、女孩、老師，和家長：

*Update* your wardrobe. 你的服裝要跟得上時代。
*Upgrade* your apartment. 要改善你的公寓。
*Undertake a challenge.* 要承擔一項挑戰。

Learn *useful* skills. 要學會有用的技術。
Be honest and *upright.* 要非常正直。
Be a *unique* individual. 要做一個獨特的人。

Be an *understanding* person.
要做一個能體諒的人。
Be indifferent and *uncomplaining.*
要不在乎、不抱怨。
*Seek unity* among your friends.
要促進朋友之間的團結，和睦相處。

*These are keys to happiness.* 這些就是快樂的關鍵。

## III. 短篇作文：

### Keys to Happiness

Imagine that happiness is behind a series of locked doors. All you need is the right set of keys to open them. Here are a few to get you started. *First of all*, *update* your hairstyle. *Upgrade* your living conditions. *At the same time*, *undertake a challenge*. *Additionally*, *be* a *useful* person. Be honest and *upright*. Have a *unique* outlook on life. *However*, be *understanding* and reasonable. Be an *uncomplaining* person. *Above all*, *seek unity* within the community and you'll be that much closer to happiness.

### 快樂的關鍵

　　想像一下，快樂就在一連串上鎖的門後。你所需要的，就是一套正確的鑰匙來打開它們。以下有一些能讓你開始。首先，你的髮型要跟得上時代。要改善你的生活環境。同時，要承擔一項挑戰。此外，要做一個有用的人。要非常正直。要有獨特的人生觀。然而，要通情達理。要做一個不會抱怨的人。最重要的是，在社區中要尋求團結一致，那樣你就會離快樂更近了。

　　* locked〔lɑkt〕 *adj.* 鎖上的　　outlook〔'aʊt,lʊk〕 *n.* 看法
　　reasonable〔'riznəbl〕 *adj.* 合理的；理智的；通情達理的

## IV. 填空：

　　___1___ your wardrobe will certainly give you some perspective. Likewise, ___2___ your apartment. And then ___3___ a new project.

　　On top of that, learn some ___4___ skills that will serve you in the future. Be honest and ___5___. Be a ___6___ individual.

　　Most importantly, be an ___7___ person. Be indifferent and ___8___. Indeed, seeking ___9___ among your friends is one of the main keys to happiness.

　　使你的服裝跟得上時代，一定能給你一些正確的眼光。同樣地，要改善你的公寓。然後，要開始做一項新的計劃。

　　此外，要學習一些對你將來有幫助的有用技術。要非常正直。要做一個獨特的人。

　　最重要的是，要做一個能體諒的人。要不在乎、不抱怨。的確，促進朋友之間的團結，和諧相處，是快樂主要的關鍵之一。

　　【解答】 1. Updating　2. upgrade　3. undertake　4. useful　5. upright
　　　　　　6. unique　7. understanding　8. uncomplaining　9. unity
　　* perspective〔pə'spɛktɪv〕 *n.* 正確的眼光
　　project〔'prɑdʒɛkt〕 *n.* 計劃　　serve〔sɝv〕 *v.* 對（某人）有用
　　indifferent〔ɪn'dɪfrənt〕 *adj.* 漠不關心的；不在乎的

## V. 詞彙題：

***Directions:*** *Choose the one word that best completes the sentence.*

1. Has it been a while since you've _____ your look?
   (A) updated   (B) urged   (C) unpacked   (D) unlocked

2. How much would it cost to _____ from economy to business class?
   (A) uphold   (B) upload   (C) upgrade   (D) unfold

3. You'll need all your courage to _____ an impossible task.
   (A) underestimate   (B) underline   (C) undermine
   (D) undertake

4. It's common knowledge that a _____ person is always in demand.
   (A) ultimate   (B) useful   (C) usual   (D) unanimous

5. You'll never cause trouble if you're an _____ person.
   (A) upright   (B) upset   (C) upper   (D) upward

6. Each one of us has something that makes us _____.
   (A) united   (B) universal   (C) urban   (D) unique

7. The _____ person knows that everybody has a struggle.
   (A) understanding   (B) understandable   (C) utter   (D) utmost

8. Build your reputation on an _____ attitude.
   (A) used   (B) ugly   (C) uncomplaining   (D) upbringing

9. Everything goes smoothly when there's _____ within the group.
   (A) umpire   (B) unity   (C) utility   (D) usage

【答案】 1.(A)   2.(C)   3.(D)   4.(B)   5.(A)   6.(D)
　　　　 7.(A)   8.(C)   9.(B)

## VI. 同義字整理：

1. **update** 〔 ʌp'det 〕 *v.* 更新
   - = renew 〔 rɪ'nju 〕
   - = revise 〔 rɪ'vaɪz 〕
   - = modernize 〔'mɑdən,aɪz 〕
   - = bring up to date

2. **upgrade** 〔'ʌp'gred 〕 *v.* 使升級
   - = better 〔'bɛtə 〕
   - = improve 〔 ɪm'pruv 〕
   - = enhance 〔 ɪn'hæns 〕

3. **undertake** 〔,ʌndə'tek 〕*v.* 承擔；
   從事
   - = try 〔 traɪ 〕
   - = begin 〔 bɪ'gɪn 〕
   - = attempt 〔 ə'tɛmpt 〕
   - = take on
   - = endeavor to do

4. **useful** 〔'jusfəl 〕 *adj.* 有用的
   - = helpful 〔'hɛlpfəl 〕
   - = valuable 〔'væljʊəbl̩ 〕
   - = practical 〔'præktɪkl̩ 〕
   - = effective 〔 ə'fɛktɪv 〕

5. **upright** 〔'ʌp,raɪt 〕 *adj.* 正直的
   - = honest 〔'ɑnɪst 〕
   - = just 〔 dʒʌst 〕
   - = faithful 〔'feθfəl 〕
   - = ethical 〔'ɛθɪkl̩ 〕
   - = honorable 〔'ɑnərəbl̩ 〕

6. **unique** 〔 ju'nik 〕 *adj.* 獨特的
   - = distinct 〔 dɪ'stɪŋkt 〕
   - = special 〔'spɛʃəl 〕
   - = exclusive 〔 ɪk'sklusɪv 〕
   - = unmatched 〔 ʌn'mætʃt 〕
   - = unparalleled 〔 ʌn'pærə,lɛld 〕
   - = incomparable
     〔 ɪn'kɑmpərəbl̩ 〕

7. **understanding**
   〔,ʌndə'stændɪŋ 〕 *adj.* 能諒解的
   - = sympathetic 〔,sɪmpə'θɛtɪk 〕
   - = compassionate
     〔 kəm'pæʃənɪt 〕
   - = considerate 〔 kən'sɪdərɪt 〕
   - = sensitive 〔'sɛnsətɪv 〕
   - = patient 〔'peʃənt 〕

8. **uncomplaining**
   〔,ʌnkəm'plenɪŋ 〕 *adj.* 不抱怨的
   - = not complaining
   - = showing patience and
     tolerance

9. **unity** 〔'junətɪ 〕 *n.* 統一；（團結）
   一致
   - = agreement 〔 ə'grimənt 〕
   - = consensus 〔 kən'sɛnsəs 〕
   - = harmony 〔'hɑrmənɪ 〕
   - = solidarity 〔,sɑlə'dærətɪ 〕

U

**How to Be Happy**

# 22. V

| 看英文唸出中文 | 一口氣說九句 | 看中文唸出英文 |
| --- | --- | --- |

**victory** [2]
〔'vɪktrɪ〕 *n.*

**victorious** [6]
〔vɪk'torɪəs〕 *adj.*

**victor** [6]
〔'vɪktɚ〕 *n.*

詞類變化

Seek *victory*.
要追求勝利。

Be *victorious*.
要勝利。

A *victor*.
要成為勝利者。

勝利

勝利的

勝利者

---

**volleyball** [2]
〔'valɪ,bɔl〕 *n.*

**video games**
〔'vɪdɪ,o 'gemz〕

**violin** [2]
〔,vaɪə'lɪn〕 *n.*

字首是 vi

Play *volleyball*.
要打排球。

*Video games*.
打電玩遊戲。

The *violin*.
拉小提琴。

排球

電玩遊戲

小提琴

---

**vacation** [2]
〔ve'keʃən〕 *n.*

**voyage** [4]
〔'vɔɪ·ɪdʒ〕 *n.*

**various** [3]
〔'vɛrɪəs〕 *adj.*

Go on *vacation*.
去度假。

A *voyage*.
去旅行。

Have *various* interests.
要有各種不同的興趣。

假期

旅行；航行

各種不同的

## I. 背景說明：

*Seek victory*. ( = *Try to win*. ) *Seek victory* in everything you do. ( 做什麼事都要追求勝利。) *Seek victory* and be happy. ( 追求勝利會使你快樂。) *Be victorious*. ( = *Be a victorious person*. ) *Be victorious* in all things you do. ( 做什麼事都要勝利。) *A victor*. 在此指 Be *a victor*. ( 要成為勝利者。) Be *a victor* in all you attempt to do. ( 你想要做什麼事，都要成為勝利者。) Be *a victor* and a winner. ( 要做一個贏家。)

*Play volleyball*. 可說成：*Playing volleyball* will make you happy. ( 打排球會使你快樂。) *Playing volleyball* is good exercise. ( 打排球是很好的運動。) 「play + 運動名稱」，不加定冠詞 the。在此 exercise 不可說成 *an exercise* ( 誤 )。*Video games*. 在此指 Play *video games*. ( 要打電玩遊戲。) Playing *video games* is fun, but don't get addicted to it. ( 打電玩遊戲很有趣，但不要上癮。) When you're in a bad mood, play *video games*. ( 當你心情不好的時候，可以打電玩遊戲。) *The violin*. 在此指 Play *the violin*. ( 要拉小提琴。) 可說成：Learn to play *the violin*. ( 要學拉小提琴。) Take a *violin* class. ( 要上小提琴課。)

*Go on vacation*. ( = *Go on a vacation*. ) If you're not happy, just *go on vacation*. ( 如果你不快樂，去度假就對了。) Everyone should *go on vacation* once in a while. ( 每個人都應該偶爾去度假。) *A voyage*. 可說成：Going on *a voyage* is an unusual experience. ( 去航行是一種不尋常的經驗。) Going on *a voyage* may cost a lot of money. ( 去航行可能會花很多錢。) Go on *a voyage*. 可指「去航行。」或「去旅行。」不一定是坐船。*Have various interests*. 可說成：Everyone should *have various interests*. ( 每個人都應該有各種不同的興趣。) *Having various interests* will make you happy. ( 有各種不同的興趣會使你快樂。)

**V**

## II. 英語演講：

### 【一字英語演講】

*Welcome:*

*Seek victory.*
*Be victorious.*
*A victor.*

*Play volleyball.*
*Video games.*
*The violin.*

*Go on vacation.*
*A voyage.*
*Have various*
*interests.*

*Do this, and you'll*
*be incredibly*
*happy.*

### 【短篇英語演講】

*Welcome:* 歡迎大家：

*Seek victory* in everything you do.
做什麼事都要追求勝利。
*Be victorious* and righteous. 要勝利又正直。
Be *a victor* and a winner. 要做一個贏家。

*Playing volleyball* is good exercise.
打排球是很好的運動。
Play some *video games*. 要打一些電玩遊戲。
Learn to play *the violin*. 要學拉小提琴。

Everyone should *go on vacation* once in a while.
每個人都應該偶爾去度假。
Going on *a voyage* is an unusual experience.
去航行是一種不尋常的經驗。
*Having various interests* will keep you busy.
有各種不同的興趣會使你忙碌。

*Do this, and you'll be incredibly happy.*
這麼做，你就會非常快樂。

V

## III. 短篇作文：

### How to Be Incredibly Happy

There is an incredible amount of happiness available to you.
*For one thing*, be a person who *seeks victory*. *Be* a *victorious* person.
Be *a victor* in all you attempt to do. *Besides, playing volleyball* will
make you happy. *On the other hand*, playing *video games* is fun, but
don't get addicted to it. *So*, take a *violin* class. *Or*, if you're not
happy, just *go on vacation*. Going on *a voyage* may cost a lot of
money, but it will be worth it. *At any rate, having various interests*
will make you incredibly happy.

### 如何才能非常快樂

　　你可以獲得相當多的快樂。首先，要做一個追求勝利的人。要勝利。你想要做什麼事，都要成爲勝利者。此外，打排球會使你快樂。另一方面，打電玩遊戲很有趣，但不要上癮。所以，要上小提琴課。或者，如果你不快樂，去度假就對了。去航行可能會花很多錢，但卻是很值得的。無論如何，有各種不同的興趣會使你非常快樂。

* incredibly〔ɪnˈkrɛdəblɪ〕*adv.* 非常地
incredible〔ɪnˈkrɛdəbḷ〕*adj.* 令人無法置信的
available〔əˈveləbḷ〕*adj.* 可獲得的
attempt〔əˈtɛmpt〕*v.* 企圖；嘗試
addicted〔əˈdɪktɪd〕*adj.* 上癮的　　***at any rate*** 無論如何

## IV. 填空：

　　To be incredibly happy, seek ___1___ in everything you do. Be ___2___ and righteous.　Be a ___3___ and a winner.

　　On top of that, playing ___4___ is good exercise.　Play some ___5___ games.　Maybe even learn to play the ___6___.

　　For sure, everyone should go on ___7___.　Going on a ___8___ is an unusual experience.　Having ___9___ interests will keep you busy and happy.

　　要非常快樂，做什麼事都要追求勝利。要勝利又正直。要做一個贏家。

　　此外，打排球是很好的運動。要打一些電玩遊戲。或許甚至要學拉小提琴。

　　每個人確實都應該去度假。去航行是一種不尋常的經驗。有各種不同的興趣會使你忙碌又快樂。

【解答】1. victory　2. victorious　3. victor　4. volleyball
　　　　5. video　6. violin　7. vacation　8. voyage
　　　　9. various
* righteous〔ˈraɪtʃəs〕*adj.* 正直的　　***for sure*** 確實地；當然

## V. 詞彙題：

***Directions:*** *Choose the one word that best completes the sentence.*

1. By working hard and staying focused, _____ can be yours.
   (A) victory   (B) vapor   (C) variation   (D) vegetation

2. To be _____, you must fight until the bitter end.
   (A) vain   (B) vague   (C) vacant   (D) victorious

3. Experience the joy of being a _____.
   (A) victim   (B) victor   (C) vigor   (D) volcano

4. If you're bored, you could play a game of _____ with your friends.
   (A) verge   (B) valley   (C) volleyball   (D) village

5. _____ are fun and good exercise for your mind.
   (A) Video games   (B) Videotapes   (C) Vacancies
   (D) Volumes

6. The _____ makes such a beautiful sound when played properly.
   (A) vanilla   (B) vehicle   (C) violin   (D) violet

7. If you've been overworked lately, maybe you need a _____.
   (A) version   (B) vacation   (C) virus   (D) vowel

8. Everybody should go on a long _____ at least once in life.
   (A) vanity   (B) vase   (C) vaccine   (D) voyage

9. Having _____ interests will keep your body active and your mind sharp.
   (A) various   (B) verbal   (C) vertical   (D) vicious

【答案】 1.(A)   2.(D)   3.(B)   4.(C)   5.(A)   6.(C)
         7.(B)   8.(D)   9.(A)

## VI. 同義字整理：

1. **victory** 〔'vɪktrɪ 〕 *n.* 勝利
   - = win 〔 wɪn 〕
   - = success 〔 sək'sɛs 〕
   - = triumph 〔'traɪəmf 〕
   - = mastery 〔'mæstərɪ 〕

2. **victorious** 〔 vɪk'torɪəs 〕 *adj.* 勝利的
   - = winning 〔'wɪnɪŋ 〕
   - = successful 〔 sək'sɛsfəl 〕
   - = triumphant 〔 traɪ'ʌmfənt 〕

   - = conquering 〔'kɑŋkərɪŋ 〕
   - = prizewinning 〔'praɪz,wɪnɪŋ 〕

3. **victor** 〔'vɪktɚ 〕 *n.* 勝利者
   - = winner 〔'wɪnɚ 〕
   - = champion 〔'tʃæmpɪən 〕
   - = conqueror 〔'kɑŋkərɚ 〕
   - = prizewinner 〔'praɪz,wɪnɚ 〕

4. **volleyball** 〔'vɑlɪ,bɔl 〕 *n.* 排球
   - = a game in which two teams hit an inflated ball over a high net using their hands

5. **video games** 電玩遊戲
   - = any of various games that can be played by using an electronic control to move points of light or graphical symbols on the screen of a visual display unit

6. **violin** 〔,vaɪə'lɪn 〕 *n.* 小提琴
   - = a type of musical instrument with four strings, played with a bow

7. **vacation** 〔 ve'keʃən 〕 *n.* 假期
   - = holiday 〔'hɑlə,de 〕
   - = leave 〔 liv 〕
   - = time off

8. **voyage** 〔'vɔɪ•ɪdʒ 〕 *n.* 旅行；航行
   - = journey 〔'dʒɝnɪ 〕
   - = trip 〔 trɪp 〕
   - = a long journey to a foreign or distant place, especially by sea

9. **various** 〔'vɛrɪəs 〕 *adj.* 各種不同的
   - = varied 〔'vɛrɪd 〕
   - = assorted 〔 ə'sɔrtɪd 〕
   - = diverse 〔 daɪ'vɝs 〕

   - = different 〔'dɪfrənt 〕
   - = miscellaneous 〔,mɪsl̩'enɪəs 〕

**V**

## How to Be Happy

# 23. W

| 看英文唸出中文 | 一口氣說九句 | 看中文唸出英文 |
|---|---|---|

**walk**[1]
〔wɔk〕*v.*

**whistle**[3]
〔'hwɪsḷ〕*v.*

**wonder**[2]
〔'wʌndɚ〕*v.*

三個動詞

*Walk.*
要走路。

*Whistle.*
吹口哨。

*Wonder.*
要有好奇心。

走路

吹口哨

想知道

---

**water**[1]
〔'wɔtɚ〕*n.*

**wine**[1]
〔waɪn〕*n.*

**whisky**[5]
〔'hwɪskɪ〕*n.*

三種飲料

Drink *water.*
要喝水。

*Wine.*
要喝葡萄酒。

*Whisky.*
要喝威士忌。

水

葡萄酒

威士忌

---

**wealthy**[3]
〔'wɛlθɪ〕*adj.*

**welcoming**[1]
〔'wɛlkəmɪŋ〕*adj.*

**wealth**[3]
〔wɛlθ〕*n.*

字首都是 we

Be *wealthy.*
要富有。

*Welcoming.*
要好客。

Share your *wealth.*
要分享你的財富。

詞類變化

有錢的

好客的

財富

## I. 背景說明：

　　*Walk*. 可説成：Take a *walk*.（要散步。）（ = *Go for a walk*.）
*Walking* is great for us.（散步對我們有好處。）*Walking* is
extremely healthy.（散步非常有益健康。）*Whistle*. 可説成：
When you're happy, you'll *whistle* while walking.（當你快樂的
時候，你會邊走路邊吹口哨。）*Whistle* a pleasant melody.（要用
口哨吹出令人愉快的旋律。）*Wonder*.（ = *Be curious*.）*Wonder*
about things.（對事情要好奇。）（ = *Be curious about things*.）
*Wonder* about the future.（要對未來好奇。）（ = *Be curious about
the future*.）wonder 的主要意思是「覺得驚奇」，它的形容詞是
wonderful（很棒的），在這裡作「不知道，想知道」解。美國人
借錢的時候，習慣説：I was *wondering* if you can lend me
some money.（不知道你是否可以借我一些錢。）

　　*Drink water*. 可説成：*Drink* plenty of *water*.（要喝很多
水。）（ = *Drink lots of water*.）喝水會使人快樂，但水要慢慢
喝，早上起來喝兩杯溫開水，有助於身體健康。記住，永遠不
要讓自己有口渴的感覺，口渴時，即表示身體在受到傷害。
*Wine*. 在此指 Drink *wine*.（要喝葡萄酒。）*Wine* is made from
grapes.（葡萄酒是由葡萄製成。）A little bit of *wine* is good for
you.（一點葡萄酒對你有好處。）*Whisky*. 在此指 Drink *whisky*.
（要喝威士忌。）*Whisky* is made from grains.（威士忌是由穀物
製成。）Drink a shot of *whisky*.（要喝一小口威士忌。）（ = *Have
a small amount of whisky*.）【shot〔ʃɑt〕*n.* 一小杯；一小口（烈酒）】
wine（葡萄酒）的酒精濃度是 12%～15%，whisky（威士忌）
較烈，酒精濃度是 40%～70%，beer（啤酒）的酒精濃度則是
3%～8%。

W

*Be wealthy.* ( = *Be a wealthy person.* 要做個有錢人。)
*Be wealthy* and prosperous. ( 要既富有又成功。) *Welcoming.*
在此指 Be *welcoming.* ( 要好客。)( = *Be hospitable.* ) Have
a *welcoming* attitude. ( 要有好客的態度。) Be a *welcoming*
person. ( 要做一個好客的人。) 請客吃飯絕對會讓你快樂，以
後賺的錢會比花費的多。 *Share your wealth.* ( = *Be generous.*
要慷慨。) *Share your wealth* with your friends. ( 要和朋友分
享你的財富。) *Share your wealth* with your family. ( 要和家
人分享你的財富。)

*What a good-looking crowd:*

Walk.
Whistle.
Wonder.

Drink water.
Wine.
Whisky.

Be wealthy.
Welcoming.
Share your wealth.

*Follow this path to happiness.*

## Ⅱ. 短篇英語演講：

***What a good-looking crowd:*** 多麼好看的一群人啊：

***Walking*** is extremely healthy. 散步非常有益健康。
When you're happy, you'll ***whistle*** while walking.
當你快樂的時候，你會邊走路邊吹口哨。
***Wonder*** about the future. 要對未來好奇。

***Drink*** plenty of ***water***. 要喝很多水。
A little bit of ***wine*** is good for you. 一點葡萄酒對你有好處。
Drink a shot of ***whisky***. 要喝一小口威士忌。

***Be wealthy*** and prosperous. 要既富有又成功。
Be a ***welcoming*** person. 要做一個好客的人。
***Share your wealth*** with your friends.
要和朋友分享你的財富。

***Follow this path to happiness***. 要遵循這個快樂之道。

## Ⅲ. 短篇作文：

### The Path to Happiness

　　Besides being good exercise, ***walking*** is the path to happiness. ***Whistle*** a pleasant melody while you stroll down the sidewalk. *Likewise*, ***wonder*** about things. *Meanwhile*, ***drink*** lots of ***water***. A glass of ***wine*** is good for your heart. A shot of ***whisky*** will lift your spirits. *On the other hand*, ***be*** a ***wealthy*** person. Have a ***welcoming*** attitude. *Above all*, ***share your wealth*** with your family and you'll be on the path to happiness.

W

### 快樂之道

　　散步除了是很好的運動之外，也是快樂之道。當你沿著人行道漫步時，要用口哨吹出令人愉快的旋律。同樣地，對事情要好奇。同時，要喝很多水。一杯紅酒對你的心臟有益。一小口威士忌能提振你的精神。另一方面，要做個有錢人。要有好客的態度。最重要的是，要和家人分享你的財富，那你就會走上快樂之路。

　　* path〔pæθ〕*n.* ( 人生的 ) 道路
　　melody〔'mɛlədɪ〕*n.* 旋律　　　stroll〔strol〕*v.* 漫步
　　sidewalk〔'saɪd,wɔk〕*n.* 人行道　　lift〔lɪft〕*v.* 提振

## IV. 填空：

　　　　1　　 is extremely healthy.  When you're happy, you'll
　　2　　 while walking.  Of course, 　　3　　 about the future.

　　Additionally, make sure to stay hydrated by drinking plenty
of 　　4　　.  A little bit of 　　5　　 is good for you.  Drink a shot
of 　　6　　.

　　Most importantly, be 　　7　　.  Be a 　　8　　 person.  And get
on the path to happiness by sharing your 　　9　　 with your friends.

　　散步非常有益健康。當你快樂的時候，你會邊走邊吹口哨。當然，要對未來好奇。

　　此外，要喝許多的水，以確保有飲用足夠的水。一點葡萄酒對你有好處。要喝一小口威士忌。

　　最重要的是，要富有。要做一個好客的人。並且藉由和朋友分享你的財富，走上快樂之路。

【解答】 1. Walking　2. whistle　3. wonder　4. water　5. wine
　　　　6. whisky　7. wealthy　8. welcoming　9. wealth
　　　　* extremely〔ɪk'strimlɪ〕*adv.* 非常地
　　　　hydrate〔'haɪ,dret〕*v.* 為…補水
　　　　***keep hydrated*** 保持足量飲用水

## V. 詞彙題：

*Directions: Choose the one word that best completes the sentence.*

1. Whenever you're feeling stressed out, go for a _____ around the block.

   (A) wage　(B) walk　(C) waist　(D) weapon

2. If you hear someone _____, you know they're happy.

   (A) warning　(B) weeping　(C) wailing　(D) whistling

3. I was just _____ where to spend the weekend

   (A) wondering　(B) weaving　(C) withdrawing　(D) whirling

4. You should drink at least 8 glasses of _____ per day.

   (A) ware　(B) warmth　(C) water　(D) wax

5. _____ is made from grapes.

   (A) Wildlife　(B) Width　(C) Weight　(D) Wine

6. _____ is made from grains.

   (A) Wilderness　(B) Whisky　(C) Worship　(D) Wisdom

7. To be _____ is the dream of every person on Earth.

   (A) wary　(B) western　(C) willing　(D) wealthy

8. Your _____ personality will attract many admirers.

   (A) windy　(B) wooden　(C) welcoming　(D) widespread

9. What good is your _____ if you don't share it with others?

   (A) wealth　(B) wave　(C) wing　(D) wreath

【答案】　1. ( B )　2. ( D )　3. ( A )　4. ( C )　5. ( D )　6. ( B )
　　　　　7. ( D )　8. ( C )　9. ( A )

W

## VI. 同義字整理：

1. **walk** 〔 wɔk 〕 *v.* 走路
   - = stride 〔 straɪd 〕
   - = stroll 〔 strol 〕
   - = go on foot
   - = travel on foot

2. **whistle** 〔 'hwɪsḷ 〕 *v.* 吹口哨
   - = to make a high clear musical sound or a series of such sounds by forcing the breath through puckered lips or through the teeth

3. **wonder** 〔 'wʌndə 〕 *v.* 想知道
   - = speculate 〔 'spɛkjə,let 〕
   - = ponder 〔 'pandə 〕
   - = meditate 〔 'mɛdə,tet 〕

   - = be curious
   - = be inquisitive

4. **water** 〔 'wɔtə 〕 *n.* 水
   - = liquid 〔 'lɪkwɪd 〕
   - = aqua 〔 'ækwə 〕

5. **wine** 〔 waɪn 〕 *n.* 葡萄酒
   - = a beverage made of the fermented juice of any of various kinds of grapes, usually containing from 10 to 15 percent alcohol by volume

6. **whisky** 〔 'hwɪskɪ 〕 *n.* 威士忌
   - = Scotch 〔 skɑtʃ 〕
   - = malt 〔 mɔlt 〕
   - = rye 〔 raɪ 〕

   - = bourbon 〔 'burbən 〕
   - = firewater 〔 'faɪr,wɔtə 〕

7. **wealthy** 〔 'wɛlθɪ 〕 *adj.* 有錢的
   - = rich 〔 rɪtʃ 〕
   - = prosperous 〔 'praspərəs 〕
   - = affluent 〔 'æfluənt 〕
   - = well-off 〔 'wɛl,ɔf 〕

8. **welcoming** 〔 'wɛlkəmɪŋ 〕 *adj.* 好客的
   - = cordial 〔 'kɔrdʒəl 〕
   - = warm 〔 wɔrm 〕
   - = friendly 〔 'frɛndlɪ 〕
   - = accepting 〔 ək'sɛptɪŋ 〕

9. **wealth** 〔 wɛlθ 〕 *n.* 財富
   - = riches 〔 'rɪtʃɪz 〕
   - = fortune 〔 'fɔrtʃən 〕
   - = affluence 〔 'æfluəns 〕

   - = means 〔 minz 〕
   - = possessions 〔 pə'zɛʃənz 〕

**W**

# How to Be Happy

# *24.* Y , Z

| 看英文唸出中文 | 一口氣說九句 | 看中文唸出英文 |
|---|---|---|

**yam**[1]
〔 jæm 〕 *n.*

Eat *yams*.
要吃山藥。

山藥

**yogurt**[4]
〔ˋjogɚt 〕 *n.*

*Yogurt*.
要吃優格。

優格

**yummy**[1]
〔ˋjʌmɪ 〕 *adj.*

*Yummy* food.
要吃美食。

好吃的

---

**yoga**[5]
〔ˋjogə 〕 *n.*

字首是 yo

Try *yoga*.
要嘗試瑜珈。

瑜伽

**young**[1]
〔 jʌŋ 〕 *adj.*

Be *young*.
要年輕。

年輕的

**youthful**[4]
〔ˋjuθfəl 〕 *adj.*

*Youthful*.
要年輕。

年輕的

---

**zeal**[6]
〔 zil 〕 *n.*

Have *zeal*.
要有熱忱。

熱忱

**yard**[2]
〔 jɑrd 〕 *n.*

字首是 ya

A *yard*.
要有院子。

院子

**yacht**[5]
〔 jɑt 〕 *n.*

A *yacht*.
要有遊艇。

遊艇

**Y**

## I. 背景説明：

*Eat yams*.（= *Eat Chinese yams*. ）yam 是「山藥」或「白色蕃薯」，「黄色蕃薯；紅色蕃薯」是 sweet potato。可説成：*Eating yams* will make you healthy.（吃山藥會使你健康。）*Yogurt*. 在此指 Eat *yogurt*.（要吃優格。）Eat *yogurt* daily.（要每天吃優格。）Eating *yogurt* will make you strong.（吃優格會使你身體強壯。）*Yummy food*. 在此指 Eat *yummy food*.（要吃美食。）Eat *yummy food* and be happy.（吃美食就會快樂。）Eat *yummy food* with your friends.（要和你的朋友吃美食。）

*Try yoga*. 可説成：Take a *yoga* class.（要上瑜珈課。）Practice *yoga*.（要做瑜珈。）（= *Do yoga*. ）*Be young*. 可説成：*Be young* at heart.（要有年輕的心。）（= *Be childlike*. ）*Be young* in mind.（心態要年輕。）（= *Be curious and thirsty for knowledge*. 要有好奇心，求知若渴。）*Youthful*. 在此指 Be *youthful*.（要有年輕人的樣子。）（= *Be an active person*. ）Have a *youthful* attitude.（要有年輕的心態。）Be *youthful* and energetic.（要像年輕人一樣精力充沛。）

*Have zeal*.（= *Have enthusiasm*. = *Have passion*. ）*Have zeal* for life.（對生活要有熱忱。）*Have zeal* for everything you do.（對你所做的每一件事都要有熱忱。）zeal 可作「熱忱」或「熱心」解。*A yard*. 在此指 Have *a yard*.（要有院子。）The bigger *a yard* you have, the happier you are.（院子越大，你會越快樂。）*A yacht*. 在此指 Have *a yacht*.（要有遊艇。）Spend some time on *a yacht*.（要在遊艇上享受一下。）Go to a party on *a yacht*.（要去參加遊艇上的派對。）在遊艇上狂歡，非常愉快，因爲空氣好、風景好、氣氛好。

## II. 英語演講：

| 【一字英語演講】 | 【短篇英語演講】 |
|---|---|
| *Dear friends:* | *Dear friends:* 親愛的朋友： |
| | |
| *Eat yams.* | *Eating yams* will make you healthy. |
| *Yogurt.* | 吃山藥會使你健康。 |
| *Yummy food.* | Eating *yogurt* will make you strong. |
| | 吃優格會使你身體強壯。 |
| *Try yoga.* | Eat *yummy food* with your friends. |
| *Be young.* | 要和你的朋友吃美食。 |
| *Youthful.* | |
| | Take a *yoga* class. 要上瑜珈課。 |
| *Have zeal.* | *Be young* at heart. 要有年輕的心。 |
| *A yard.* | Be *youthful* and energetic. |
| *A yacht.* | 要像年輕人一樣精力充沛。 |
| | |
| *Do this, and* | *Have zeal* for life. 對生活要有熱忱。 |
| *you'll be happy.* | Have *a yard*. 要有院子。 |
| | Spend some time on *a yacht*. 要在遊艇上享受一下。 |
| | |
| | *Do this, and you'll be happy.* |
| | 這麼做，你就會快樂。 |

## III. 短篇作文：

### Be Happy

I know you want to be happy just as much as anyone. So, please take my advice. *First of all*, enjoy a serving of *yams*. Eat *yogurt* daily. Eat *yummy food* and be happy. *On the other hand*, *try yoga*. *Be young* in mind. Have a *youthful* attitude. *In a similar way*, *have zeal* for everything you do. The bigger *a yard* you have, the happier you are. And if you ever get the chance, go to a party on *a yacht*. *For sure*, you'll be the happiest person alive.

### 要快樂

我知道你就像任何人一樣，想要快樂。所以，請聽從我的勸告。首先，要享用一份山藥。要每天吃優格。吃美食就會快樂。另一方面，要嘗試瑜珈。心態要年輕。要有年輕的心態。同樣地，對你所做的每一件事都要有熱忱。院子越大，你會越快樂。而且如果有機會，要去參加遊艇上的派對。你一定會成為全世界最快樂的人。

* take 〔 tek 〕 v. 聽從    serving 〔'sɜvɪŋ〕 n. 一份
「the + 比較級…the + 比較級」表「越…就越~」。
ever 〔'ɛvə〕 adv. 在任何時候    *for sure* 肯定地；無疑地

## IV. 填空：

To start with, eating ___1___ will make you healthy. Eating ___2___ will make you strong. Eat ___3___ food with your friends.

You might be surprised by how happy you'll be when you take a ___4___ class. Likewise, be ___5___ at heart. Be ___6___ and energetic.

Most importantly, have ___7___ for life. Have a nice big ___8___ . And of course, spend some time on a ___9___ .

首先，吃山藥會使你健康。吃優格會使你身體強壯。要和你的朋友吃美食。

你可能會很驚訝，當你上瑜珈課時，你會如此快樂。同樣地，心態要年輕。要像年輕人一樣精力充沛。

最重要的是，對生活要有熱忱。要有一個又大又好的院子。而且當然要在遊艇上享受一下。

【解答】 1. yams   2. yogurt   3. yummy   4. yoga   5. young
6. youthful   7. zeal   8. yard   9. yacht
* energetic 〔ˌɛnə'dʒɛtɪk〕 adj. 充滿活力的

## V. 詞彙題：

***Directions:*** *Choose the one word that best completes the sentence.*

1. In many countries, sweet potatoes are often referred to as
   "_____".
   (A) exams　(B) grams　(C) dams　(D) yams

2. _____ is common in Nepal, where it is served as both an
   appetizer and dessert.
   (A) Yogurt　(B) Yolk　(C) Yarn　(D) Yeast

3. Only the _____ foods can make us truly happy.
   (A) yellow　(B) yearly　(C) yummy　(D) yucky

4. Practicing _____ is a great way to fight stress and anxiety.
   (A) soda　(B) yoga　(C) agenda　(D) panda

5. You should enjoy life while you're _____, because it only
   gets harder.
   (A) weak　(B) old　(C) young　(D) elder

6. People will be impressed by your _____ appearance.
   (A) meaningful　(B) lawful　(C) forgetful　(D) youthful

7. We are attracted to people with a _____ for life.
   (A) zeal　(B) seal　(C) deal　(D) meal

8. No man can be genuinely happy until he has his own back
   _____.
   (A) card　(B) yard　(C) guard　(D) board

9. Never pass up a chance to party on some rich guy's _____.
   (A) plight　(B) fright　(C) yacht　(D) weight

【答案】1.（D）　2.（A）　3.（C）　4.（B）　5.（C）　6.（D）
　　　　7.（A）　8.（B）　9.（C）

## VI. 同義字整理：

1. **yam** 〔 jæm 〕 *n.* 山藥

  = the starchy, tuberous root of any of various African climbing vines, cultivated for food in warm regions: resembling but botanically unrelated to the sweet potato

2. **yogurt** 〔 'jogɚt 〕 *n.* 優格

  = a custard-like food with a tart flavor, prepared from milk curdled by bacteria, and often sweetened or flavored

3. **yummy** 〔 'jʌmɪ 〕 *adj.* 好吃的

  = delicious 〔 dɪ'lɪʃəs 〕
  = tasty 〔 'testɪ 〕

4. **yoga** 〔 'jogə 〕 *n.* 瑜珈

  = a system of physical and mental disciplines practiced to attain control of body and mind, tranquility, etc., esp. a series of postures and breathing exercises

5. **young** 〔 jʌŋ 〕 *adj.* 年輕的

  = juvenile 〔 'dʒuvə,naɪl 〕
  = youthful 〔 'juθfəl 〕
  = adolescent 〔 ,ædl̩'ɛsn̩t 〕

6. **youthful** 〔 'juθfəl 〕 *adj.* 年輕的

  = young 〔 jʌŋ 〕
  = juvenile 〔 'dʒuvə,naɪl 〕
  = vigorous 〔 'vɪgərəs 〕

7. **zeal** 〔 zil 〕 *n.* 熱忱

  = passion 〔 'pæʃən 〕
  = devotion 〔 dɪ'voʃən 〕
  = enthusiasm 〔 ɪn'θjuzɪ,æzəm 〕

8. **yard** 〔 jɑrd 〕 *n.* 院子

  = courtyard 〔 'kort,jɑrd 〕
  = the ground that immediately adjoins or surrounds a house, public building, etc.

9. **yacht** 〔 jɑt 〕 *n.* 遊艇

  = ship 〔 ʃɪp 〕
  = boat 〔 bot 〕
  = sailboat 〔 'sel,bot 〕

Y

# INDEX・索引

※ 可利用索引，檢查你是否都認識這些字。

索引

索引

# How to Be Happy

全書 216 句

聽「英文一字金」就和聽唸經一樣，再重複不停地唸，就能脫口而出！

1. Advance.
   Attain.
   Acquire.

   Be alive.
   Animated.
   Artistic.

   Seek adventure.
   Amusement.
   Go abroad.

2. Be brave.
   Busy.
   Take a bath.

   Go barefoot.
   To the beach.
   Enjoy the breeze.

   Play baseball.
   Basketball.
   Badminton.

3. Be cheerful.
   Childlike.
   Very colorful.

   Truly curious.
   Extremely courteous.
   Exceptionally courageous.

   Seek charity.
   Community.
   Companionship.

4. Be really content.
   Very compassionate.
   Deeply conscientious.

   Charitable.
   Cooperative.
   Truly carefree.

   Celebrate life.
   Join the conversation.
   Make a contribution.

5. Be very decent.
   Decisive.
   A dancer.

   Date.
   Dream.
   Delight.

   Eat dumplings.
   Doughnuts.
   Peking duck.

6. Dance.
   Draw.
   Dare to dream.

   Have dinner.
   Dessert.
   Delicious food.

   Daydream.
   Watch DVDs.
   Go to a disco.

7. Enjoy.
Engage.
Exercise.

Be elastic.
Energetic.
Very enthusiastic.

Seek enjoyment.
Entertainment.
Enlightenment.

8. Feast.
Forget.
Be forgiving.

Focused.
Really flexible.
Very friendly.

Free.
Truly funny.
Move forward.

9. Go golfing.
To the gym.
A gallery.

Have a goal.
Have a gathering.
Play the guitar.

Be grateful.
Very generous.
A globe-trotter.

10. Have hope.
Health.
Harmony.

Humor.
A hobby.
Get a new hairdo.

Hug somebody.
Follow your heart.
Go on a holiday.

11. Be inspired.
Indifferent.
Independent.

Seek intimacy.
Interaction.
Invention.

Imagine.
Invite others.
Surf the Internet.

12. Laugh.
Stay loose.
Fall in love.

Be lovely.
Lovable.
Very logical.

Liberal.
Seek liberty.
Seek longevity.

13. Mingle.
Marry.
Be merry.

Mild.
Mature.
Mellow.

Have a massage.
A nice meal.
Watch a movie.

14. Be natural.
Naughty.
Naive.

Read a novel.
Take a nap.
Eat nutritiously.

Have lots of nerve.
Numerous friends.
Explore the neighborhood.

15. Eat organic.
Oysters.
Olives.

Go outdoors.
On an outing.
Travel overseas.

Buy an outfit.
Hit an outlet store.
Think outside the box.

16. Paint.
Party.
Seek pleasure.

Be present.
Playful.
Very peaceful.

Find a partner.
A pastime.
A pet.

17. Have a plan.
Purpose.
Project.

Be pleasant.
Practical.
Get physical.

Plant flowers.
Hit the playground.
Have a strong passion.

18. Rest.
Risk.
Be relaxed.

Realistic.
Rational.
Truly reasonable.

Seek recreation.
Refreshment.
Romance.

19. Shower.
Shop.
Sing.

Simplify.
Live simply.
Seek serenity.

Take a stroll.
Get some sun.
Go for a spin.

20. Talk.
Touch someone.
Treat somebody.

Take a tour.
Trip.
Trek.

Seek treasure.
Triumph.
A thrill.

21. Update.
Upgrade.
Undertake a challenge.

Be useful.
Upright.
Unique.

Understanding.
Uncomplaining.
Seek unity.

22. Seek victory.
Be victorious.
A victor.

Play volleyball.
Video games.
The violin.

Go on vacation.
A voyage.
Have various interests.

23. Walk.
Whistle.
Wonder.

Drink water.
Wine.
Whisky.

Be wealthy.
Welcoming.
Share your wealth.

24. Eat yams.
Yogurt.
Yummy food.

Try yoga.
Be young.
Youthful.

Have zeal.
A yard.
A yacht.

# 本書所有人

姓 名 _____  電 話 _____

地 址 _____

（如拾獲本書，請通知本人領取，感激不盡。）

## 「英文一字金④快樂幸福經」背誦記錄表

| 篇　名 | 口試通過<br>日　期 | 口試老師<br>簽　名 | 篇　名 | 口試通過<br>日　期 | 口試老師<br>簽　名 |
|---|---|---|---|---|---|
| *1.* A | | | *13.* M | | |
| *2.* B | | | *14.* N | | |
| *3.* C (1) | | | *15.* O | | |
| *4.* C (2) | | | *16.* P (1) | | |
| *5.* D (1) | | | *17.* P (2) | | |
| *6.* D (2) | | | *18.* R | | |
| *7.* E | | | *19.* S | | |
| *8.* F | | | *20.* T | | |
| *9.* G | | | *21.* U | | |
| *10.* H | | | *22.* V | | |
| *11.* I | | | *23.* W | | |
| *12.* L | | | *24.* Y, Z | | |

「財團法人臺北市一口氣英語教育基金會」
提供 *100* 萬元獎金，領完為止！

1. 每一回九句，5秒鐘內背完。

2. 每次可背多回，每天口試只限 2 次。

3. 在 1 分半鐘內，背完整本 216 句，可得獎金 2,000 元。

4. 5 分鐘內一次背完「英文一字金①～④」，可再得獎金 2,000 元。

5. 背誦地點：台北市許昌街 17 號 6F–6【一口氣英語教育基金會】

　　　TEL: (02) 2389-5212

學英文，應先從「說」開始。
會說英文，能增加自信心，
像是一件漂亮的衣服穿在身上，人人羨慕。

背「英文一字金」
是學英文的唯一方法，
只要努力，
英文有學好的一天。

「英文一字金」突破傳統，
學英文也學素養。

一個字一句話，
背佳言美句，
人生更上層樓。